SEPUP
Issue-Oriented Science

ISSUES AND LIFE SCIENCE

Ecology

THIRD EDITION
REDESIGNED FOR THE NGSS

SEPUP
Issue-Oriented Science

ISSUES AND LIFE SCIENCE

Ecology

THIRD EDITION

REDESIGNED FOR THE NGSS

THE LAWRENCE HALL OF SCIENCE
UNIVERSITY OF CALIFORNIA, BERKELEY

LaB-aiDS®

This book is part of SEPUP's *Issues and Science* course sequence. For more information about this sequence, see the SEPUP and Lab-Aids websites.

ISSUES AND EARTH SCIENCE

ISSUES AND LIFE SCIENCE

ISSUES AND PHYSICAL SCIENCE

Additional SEPUP instructional materials include:
SEPUP Modules: Grades 6–12
Science and Sustainability: Course for Grades 9–12
Science and Global Issues: Biology: Course for High School Biology

This material is based upon work supported by the National Science Foundation under Grants 9554163 and DRL1418235. Any opinions, findings, and conclusions or recommendations expressed in this material are those of the authors and do not necessarily reflect the views of the National Science Foundation.

For photo and illustration credits, see page 118, which constitutes an extension of this copyright page.

The preferred citation format for this book is SEPUP. (2017). *Issues and Life Science: Ecology.* Lawrence Hall of Science, University of California at Berkeley. Published by Lab-Aids®, Inc., Ronkonkoma, NY

Third Edition

Q4 5 6 7 8 9 10 11   22 21 20 19 18

ISBN: 978-1-63093-453-8
v3

SEPUP
Lawrence Hall of Science
University of California at Berkeley
Berkeley CA 94720-5200

e-mail: sepup@berkeley.edu
Website: www.sepuplhs.org

Published by:

LaB-aiDS®

17 Colt Court
Ronkonkoma NY 11779
Website: www.lab-aids.com

A Letter to *Issues and Life Science* Students

As you examine the activities in this book, you may wonder, "Why does this book look so different from other science books I've seen?" The reason is simple: it is a different kind of science program, and only some of what you will learn can be seen by leafing through this book!

Issues and Life Science uses several kinds of activities to teach science. As you conduct these activities, you will engage in the same practices used by scientists to understand the natural world and by engineers to solve problems. For example, you will design and conduct an experiment to investigate how genes and the environment affect the growth and development of plants. You will analyze and interpret real data to explore the effects of an introduced species. And you will model how species change over time and evolve into new species. A combination of laboratories, investigations, readings, models, scientific debates, role plays, and projects will help you develop your understanding of science and the relevance of physical science to your interests.

You will find that important scientific ideas come up again and again in different activities throughout the program. You will be expected to do more than just memorize these concepts: you will be asked to develop explanations and apply them to solve problems. In particular, you will improve your decision-making skills by using evidence to weigh outcomes and to decide what you think should be done about the scientific issues facing our society.

How do we know that this is a good way for you to learn? In general, research on science education supports it. In particular, many of the activities in this book were tested by hundreds of students and their teachers, and then modified on the basis of their feedback. New activities are based on what we learned in classrooms using the materials and on new research on science learning. In a sense, this entire book is the result of an investigation: we had people test our ideas, we interpreted the results, and we then revised our ideas! We believe the result will show you that learning more about science is important, enjoyable, and relevant to your life.

SEPUP Staff

ISSUES & LIFE SCIENCE **THIRD EDITION**

Director: Barbara Nagle

Co-Director: John Howarth

Coordinator: Janet Bellantoni

AUTHORS

Wendy Jackson, Manisha Hariani, Barbara Nagle, and Maia Willcox

OTHER CONTRIBUTORS

John Howarth

PRODUCTION

Coordination, Design, Photo Research, Composition: Seventeenth Street Studios

Production Coordinator for Lab-Aids: Hethyr Tregerman

Editing: Kerry Ouellet

FIELD TEST CENTERS

The classroom is SEPUP's laboratory for development. We are extremely appreciative of the following center directors and teachers who taught the program during the 2003–04 and 2004–05 school years. These teachers and their students contributed significantly to improving the first edition of the course. Since then, *Issues and Life Science* has been used in thousands of classrooms across the United States. This third edition is based on what we have learned from teachers and students in those classrooms. It also includes new data and information, so the issues included in the course remain fresh and up-to-date.

REGIONAL CENTER, SOUTHERN CALIFORNIA

Donna Markey, *Center Director*
 Kim Blumeyer, Helen Copeland, Pat McLoughlin, Donna Markey,
 Philip Poniktera, Samantha Swann, Miles Vandegrift

REGIONAL CENTER, IOWA

Dr. Robert Yager and Jeanne Bancroft, *Center Directors*
 Rebecca Andresen, Lore Baur, Dan Dvorak, Dan Hill, Mark Kluber, Amy Lauer,
 Lisa Martin, Stephanie Phillips

REGIONAL CENTER, WESTERN NEW YORK

Dr. Robert Horvat, *Center Director*
 Kathaleen Burke, Dick Duquin, Eleanor Falsone, Lillian Gondree, Jason Mayle,
 James Morgan, Valerie Tundo

JEFFERSON COUNTY, KENTUCKY

Pamela Boykin, *Center Director*
 Charlotte Brown, Tara Endris, Sharon Kremer, Karen Niemann,
 Susan Stinebruner, Joan Thieman

LIVERMORE, CALIFORNIA

Scott Vernoy, *Center Director*
 Rick Boster, Ann Ewing, Kathy Gabel, Sharon Schmidt, Denia Segrest,
 Bruce Wolfe

QUEENS, NEW YORK

Pam Wasserman, *Center Director*
 Gina Clemente, Cheryl Dodes, Karen Horowitz, Tricia Hutter, Jean Rogers,
 Mark Schmucker, Christine Wilk

TUCSON, ARIZONA

Jonathan Becker, *Center Director*
 Peggy Herron, Debbie Hobbs, Carol Newhouse, Nancy Webster

INDEPENDENT

Berkeley, California: Robyn McArdle
Fresno, California: Al Brofman
Orinda, California: Sue Boudreau, Janine Orr, Karen Snelson
Tucson, Arizona: Patricia Cadigan, Kevin Finegan

NGSS REVISION CENTERS

Chicago, Illinois: Sylvia Moss, Emily Reardon, Cynthia Sanchez, Victoria Taylor Burnham

Contents

Ecology

Contents

Ecology

MICHAEL LOVED TO *bike through the park. The air smelled fresher there than on the street, and he always saw so many interesting things.*

Once, he came across a bird's nest with several young chicks still in it. As he watched, one of the parents brought food for the chicks to eat. He wondered if he would see anything like that today.

Suddenly, he saw a small frog near the edge of Turtle Pond. It looked very familiar. In fact, it looked just like the frog his sister kept as a pet. It was different from the frogs he usually saw at Turtle Pond.

"Could that be my sister's frog?" Michael wondered. If it is his sister's frog, how did it get there? Did it escape or could his sister have let it go? Could a pet frog survive in Turtle Pond? How would it affect the other animals that also lived in the pond?

• • •

What are the relationships between an organism and its environment? What effect do humans have on these relationships?

In this unit, you will explore ecology: the study of the relationships between organisms—including humans—and the environment. You will practice some of the methods ecologists (scientists who study ecology) use to study the natural world, and you will develop models to help you understand and explain how ecosystems function. You will collect and analyze data about how changing one component of an ecosystem affects another, and you will have the opportunity to explore your own environment.

What causes an ecosystem to stay the same or change?

What causes some species to do well and others to decline?

How do people interact with ecosystems and their components?

These are just some of the questions that you will consider over the course of this unit. What are some questions you have about the natural world around you?

1 *The Miracle Fish?*

TALKING IT OVER

HAVE YOU EVER thought that it would be cool to have parrots flying around in your backyard? Or wished that there were hippos in your local lake? What happens when you introduce an organism into a new environment?

GUIDING QUESTIONS

How have introduced Nile perch changed Lake Victoria? What are the trade-offs of introducing Nile perch into this environment?

Fishing on Lake Victoria

James Abila is a 17-year-old Kenyan boy. His family has a small fishing boat on Lake Victoria. He sat outside his hut to talk to us. Inside, his mother was preparing lunch, while his sister and younger brother were laying out a few fish to dry in the afternoon sun.

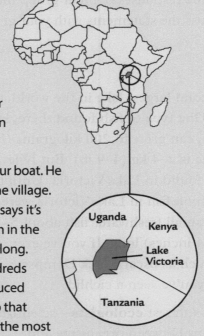

James started his story. "My father made our boat. He was always one of the best fishermen in the village. He still catches all kinds of fish, though he says it's not as easy as it used to be. Most of the fish in the lake used to be very small, just 2–4 inches long. So it was easy to use our net to catch hundreds of small fish. Then the government introduced new fish, called Nile perch, into the lake so that people could catch more fish to sell. Now, the most common fish in the lake is Nile perch. It's a much bigger fish and can be too heavy to catch with a net like my father uses. That's why I work for one of the fishing companies. They have the large boats needed to catch Nile perch. And I can earn money to help feed my family."

MATERIALS

For each student

    1 Student Sheet 1.1, "Intra-act: The Miracle Fish?"

PROCEDURE

1. Work with your group to read the story of Nile perch in Lake Victoria. Each person will experience the story from the perspective of one of four characters:

   - James
   - James's father
   - An owner of a fishing company
   - An environmentalist

2. From the perspective of your character, mark whether you agree or disagree with the statements on Student Sheet 1.1, "Intra-act: The Miracle Fish?"

3. Take turns sharing how your character responded to each statement, and circle the responses of other group members as they share them. Discuss the statements with your group.

NILE PERCH

Lake Victoria, the second largest lake in the world, contains some extremely large fish. One type of fish found there, known as Nile perch (*Lates niloticus*), can grow to 200 kilograms (kg) (440 pounds), though its average size is 2–4 kg (4–9 lb). But Nile perch weren't always found in Lake Victoria. Until the 1980s, the most common fish in Lake Victoria were cichlids (SICK-lids), small freshwater fish about 5–10 centimeters (cm) (2–4 inches) long. If you've ever seen aquarium fish, such as oscars, Jack Dempseys, or freshwater angelfish, you've seen a cichlid.

Nile perch caught in Lake Victoria

Lake Victoria cichlids interest **ecologists**—scientists who study relationships between organisms and environments—because there are so many species of these fish. Although they all belong to the same scientific family, at one time there were over 300 different species of cichlids in Lake Victoria. Almost

99% of those species could not be found anywhere else in the world!

There used to be many other kinds of fish in the lake as well, including catfish, carp, and lungfish. The 30 million people who lived around Lake Victoria relied on the lake, including the cichlids, for food. Because most of the fish were small, they could be caught by using simple fishing nets and a canoe. The fish were then dried in the sun and sold locally.

Cichlids are one of the many small types of fish commonly found in Lake Victoria.

By the late 1950s, the British government (which ruled this part of Africa at that time) grew concerned that the fish species that commercial fishers relied on were being overfished. As a result, the British government decided to introduce new fish species, such as Nile perch, into the lake. They wanted to increase the amount of fish that was available to catch and sell so that people could earn money. Ecologists were opposed to this idea. They were worried that the introduction of Nile perch, which had no natural enemies within the lake, would negatively affect the lake's ecosystem. Before a final decision could be made, Nile perch were secretly added into the lake. Eventually, more Nile perch were deliberately added by the government in the early 1960s.

During the 1960s and 1970s, before there were a lot of Nile perch in the lake, fishers caught about 100,000 metric tons of fish (including cichlids) each year. (A metric ton, also called a tonne, is 1,000 kg.) By 1989, the total catch of fish from Lake Victoria had increased to 300,000 metric tons, most of it Nile perch and almost none of it cichlids. Today, each of the three countries surrounding the lake (Uganda, Kenya, and Tanzania) sells extra fish to other countries. In the graphs on the following page, you can see how the amount of Nile perch caught has changed since 1976, and how the percentage of cichlids caught has changed over time.

Amount of Nile Perch Caught in Lake Victoria, 1976–2014

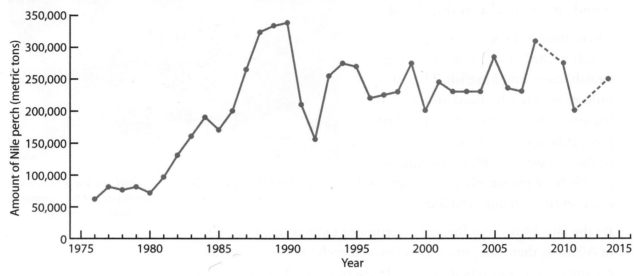

Besides increasing the amount of fish available for the commercial fishery, there have been other consequences of introducing Nile perch into the lake. Because Nile perch are large and eat other fish, they are believed to have caused the extinction of as many as 200 species of cichlids. The populations of other types of fish, including catfish and lungfish, have also declined. Many ecologists are upset that their predictions have come true.

Some of the cichlids that have become extinct ate algae. With their extinction, the amount of algae in the lake has increased five-fold. As they break down the dying algae, decomposers use up a lot of oxygen, making it difficult for other tiny plants and animals to survive in the lake. Today, many of the deeper parts of the lake are considered "dead" because they don't contain much living matter.

Cichlids And Nile Perch Caught by Commercial Fisheries on Lake Victoria in Kenya

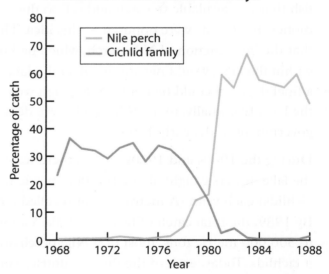

However, many of the original goals have been met. In 1979, there were 16,000 fishers along the Kenyan shores of the lake. In 1993, there were 82,300, and today there are over 200,000. Many people are now employed by companies that process and sell Nile perch overseas. Over time, these fish have brought more money into the African countries surrounding the lake. Some local people, who now eat Nile perch as part of their diet, consider Nile perch a "miracle fish." However, other local people, especially the poorest people, don't have enough to eat because there aren't enough cichlids for them to catch with nets, and they can't afford to buy the Nile perch from the big commercial fisheries.

Some ecologists wonder how long the current situation can last. Nile perch are predators. As populations of other fish decline, the Nile perch's food sources are declining. The stomachs of some large Nile perch have been found to contain smaller juvenile Nile perch. The metric tons of Nile perch caught has decreased after the peak in 1990, and in the table below, you can see that the catch per unit effort has gone down. This means that it takes more work to catch each fish—more fishers, more boats, and more time. What will happen to the population of Nile perch if their food supply decreases even further? Will the Nile perch population be overfished like the fish populations before it? Only time will tell.

Catch Per Unit Effort for Nile Perch in Lake Victoria

Year(s)	Catch rate (metric tons per year)
2000	8.8
2006	6.3
2011–2012	5.3

EXTENSION

Make a list of plants and animals around your school, home, and neighborhood. To determine which of these species are introduced and which are native to your area, use the websites and other resources on the SEPUP Third Edition Ecology page of the SEPUP website at *www.sepuplhs.org/middle/third-edition.*

ANALYSIS

1. Based on the reading, how did the amount of fish caught in Lake Victoria change from the 1960s to 1990?

2. Based on the graph showing amounts of Nile perch caught in Lake Victoria, describe how the amount of Nile perch caught changed from 1980 to 1990 and from 1990 to the present.

3. Look again at the graph. How do you think the number of metric tons of fish caught relates to the size of the total fish population from year to year? Explain your reasoning.

4. How did the introduction of Nile perch affect the people who lived near Lake Victoria?

5. What effect did the introduction of Nile perch have on cichlids and other organisms that lived in the lake?

6. What do you predict is the most likely thing to happen to the population of Nile perch over the next 20–30 years? Why?

   Hint: To write a complete answer, first state your prediction. Provide two or more pieces of evidence that support your claim, and then state why your evidence supports your claim.

7. Should humans have introduced Nile perch into Lake Victoria? Support your answer with evidence and discuss the trade-offs of your decision.

   Hint: To write a complete answer, first state your opinion. Provide two or more pieces of evidence that support your opinion. Then consider all sides of the issue, and identify the trade-offs of your decision.

2 Introduced Species

PROJECT

I NTRODUCED, NON-NATIVE, EXOTIC, and **non-indigenous** are all words used to describe species that exist outside of the species' normal range because of human activity. The Nile perch is an introduced species that was placed deliberately into Lake Victoria. In other cases, the introduction of a new species into a new environment is accidental. Consider the case of the zebra mussel, which is named for the black and white stripes found on its shell. It was accidentally introduced into the United States in the 1980s, and it is now estimated to cause up to 5 billion dollars' worth of damage each year! You will read more about this species throughout this unit.

Zebra mussels

GUIDING QUESTIONS

What effect can an introduced species have on an environment? What, if anything, can or should be done to control introduced species?

MATERIALS

For the class

  Resources: books, magazines, video, Internet access, etc.

For each student

  1 Student Sheet 2.1, "Introduced Species Research"

PROCEDURE

1. Read the fictitious news articles about real introduced species on the following pages. As directed by your teacher, decide which one species your group will research.

2. Over the next few days or weeks, find information on this species from books, magazines, videos, or the Internet. You can also go to the Ecology page of the SEPUP website at www.sepuplhs.org /middle/third-edition to link to sites with more information on species mentioned in this activity.

    Use this information to complete Student Sheet 2.1, "Introduced Species Research." You should provide the following:

    • common and scientific name of your species

    • its native and current range

    • its place in a food web

    • its effect on relationships in the new ecosystem(s)

    • its relationship to and effect on people

    • the reasons for its success

    • issues related to its future growth or spread

    Later in this unit you will use your research to create a class presentation.

Kudzu Brings Down Power Lines!

Kudzu (KUD-zoo), sometimes referred to as "the vine that ate the South," has finally pushed local patience to the limit. Properly called *Pueraria lobata*, it was first introduced in the 1920s to the southern United States as food for farm animals and to reduce soil erosion. Today, this fast-growing vine from Japan has overgrown entire forests and choked local ecosystems. Last week, the weight of kudzu vines pulled down power lines, causing a two-day power outage. Mayor Lam has called for control measures. All community members are invited to a town council meeting to consider what should be done to control this destructive vine.

Response to Tiger Mosquitoes Raises Questions

The public outcry over the worsening problem with the tiger mosquito (*Aedes albopictus*) continues. In response, the city has begun nighttime spraying of insecticide. Jesse Butler, principal of the Little Town Preschool, said, "How can the city be allowed to spray poison on the backyards where children play?" City Spokesperson Kate O'Neil told reporters that the insecticide is harmless to people. "Tiger mosquitoes are very aggressive. They are much worse than the native mosquitoes. Apart from the nuisance, tiger mosquitoes can spread diseases, such as yellow fever and Zika. We have to take action!"

O'Neil invites interested residents to attend the Camford Mosquito Abatement Board presentation on the tiger mosquito problem and possible solutions.

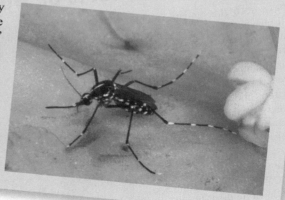

Residents Report Rats Rampant in Rockwood

It's Rockwood against the rats, and the rats seem to be winning. The number of people calling this year to complain about rats has increased from last year, according to the Rockwood Department of Streets and Sanitation. The city says the rats go for any available food source, from garbage to dog waste. That's why the city asks residents to pick up after their dogs and keep the lids on their garbage cans. But even residents who follow these guidelines continue to see more and more rats. One concerned resident said, "The problem is we can't sit out in our backyards because the rats just come from the alley, go under the fences, and scurry around all night long."

City dwellers aren't the only ones who cringe when they see rats. Farm families are also bothered when they see rats crawling into the grain bin. As the rats eat the grain, they also leave behind their waste. These offending rodents, all just one species (*Rattus norvegicus*), go by many names: house rat, barn rat, sewer rat, brown rat, and Norway rat. What many people in the United States don't realize is that these common creatures came from China long before the United States was its own country.

Aquarium Plant Turns Out to Be Worst Weed

You may have seen this aquatic plant sold in small bunches at aquarium stores. It's a popular plant because goldfish like swimming between its stems. But when aquariums are dumped out into lakes, ponds, or rivers, hydrilla (hie-DRILL-uh) can quickly grow into a dense mat that chokes out other vegetation. This change of the environment is dramatic for native animals and plants. *Hydrilla verticillata*, as it is known scientifically, can clog up city water intake valves and get tangled in boat propellers. "We used to have the best swimming hole down by the bridge," said Rita Aziz, a seventh grader at Robin Middle School. "Now it's filled with this gross weed. The last time I swam there, I got tangled in it. It was scary. I would really like to find a way to do something about it."

Flying Fish Tournament?

No, you didn't read that wrong—it's not a fly-fishing tournament but, rather, a flying fish tournament. Asian carp are so numerous in several rivers in the United States that fishers no longer need to use poles to catch them—they just motor their boats up the river and let the fish jump into the boats. Last year's winner caught 432 fish in a four-hour period. With these carp averaging 30 pounds each, that's over 12,000 pounds of fish.

This would seem like a good thing for the fishing industry, but fishers and ecologists alike are distressed by the impact these fish are having on the environment and other species of fish. One fisher complained, "I used to be able to catch largemouth bass, crappies, and sunfish. Now I hardly ever catch them, and all I see are these fish that aren't even from this river." The Fish and Wildlife Department and the sport-fishing industry are working together to try to stop the Asian carp population from growing and spreading.

A Landscape Beauty Is Taking Over

What is the link between landscaping your yard and the recent reports that local marsh species are declining? Purple loosestrife (*Lythrum salicaria*), whose magenta flowers are admired by gardeners, is the weed to blame. It was introduced from Europe as a medicinal herb in the early 1800s and is still sold today as a landscaping plant. According to Fish and Wildlife Service Ecologist Johanna Brown, "It totally takes over an area, crowding out native species. It's really devastating for fragile marsh ecosystems." Brian Van Horn, a teacher at Garden Middle School, is also concerned. "It's a tough plant to get rid of, and killing it can damage the marshes even more." A meeting at Middleton Junior High will be held to discuss this issue.

Farmers Rally to Scare Off Starlings

The recent outbreak of hog cholera may be related to starling (*Sturnus vulgaris*) droppings getting into pig food. Carol Polsky, a pig farmer in Poseyville, encouraged local farmers to work together to help get rid of

the birds. "In addition to spreading disease, those birds eat crops, seeds, and animal feed. A flock of starlings will eat just about anything, and they poop everywhere. That spreads disease to other animals, not just pigs," Polsky told reporters.

Many control options are available, according to Dr. Tony Caro of the Agricultural Sciences Board. Dr. Caro commented, "In 1891, 60 starlings were released in New York, and now they are the most common bird in America!" But a representative of the local nature society told reporters that the latest annual survey showed that starling populations had dropped since the previous year. Dr. Caro will be speaking at the next meeting of the County Farm Association, where control measures for starlings will be discussed.

Snakes on the Plains

Unlike pet dogs and cats, which get to a predictable size and then stop growing, snakes often grow much larger than their owners had expected. What do these owners do when their snakes, especially Burmese pythons, get too big to keep? Unfortunately, some people release them into the wild. In the southern part of the United States, these snakes can often survive and thrive. These pythons are literally squeezing the life out of mammalian prey and ecosystems. At first a problem only for the coastal plains in Florida, the snakes are spreading north. Willie Washington, a resident of Palmetto Park, shared, "I used to be able to let my dog out to play in my fenced backyard, but now I don't dare! My neighbor saw a snake in her backyard just last week. She called the Wildlife Depart-

ment, and when they caught it, they said it was a Burmese python and that it measured 15 feet long! I don't even want to let my children out to play." The Wildlife Department urges everyone to be on the lookout for unwanted snakes and to call them if they have a pet snake they no longer want.

ANALYSIS

1. What kinds of human activities seem to lead to problems with introduced species?

3 Data Transects

INVESTIGATION

ONE SATURDAY, KIM *and her family decided to have a picnic at the new park about 10 miles outside of town. Kim's mother had read in the community newsletter that this park was going to become a restored prairie, and she was looking forward to showing it to Kim.*

"What's a prairie and why are you interested?" asked Kim.

"A prairie is a large, open grassy area that doesn't have a lot of trees. Aunt Teresa says that this entire area used to be covered by prairie, but then people started using the land for farming, and most of the prairie is now gone. They want to bring some of the prairie back—that's what they mean by 'restoring' the prairie."

Kim wondered, "So, how is a prairie different from the grassy areas that are in the park down the street from us?"

Kim and her mother decided to ask a park ranger. The ranger explained that a prairie has plants and animals that are not normally found in other places. In the prairie that used to be where Kim and her family were standing, there had been purple coneflower, big bluestem, grasshopper sparrows, and bison.

"Wow, it would be so cool to see a bison! How come there aren't any here? Couldn't you bring some from another place?"

The ranger replied, "Before we can bring the bison back, we need to make sure that we have restored enough of the prairie to support them. One year ago, we removed all of the non-native plants by plowing the land, and then we planted seeds of native plants. Today, we are going to look at the plants to see if the native species we planted are growing and if the plants that aren't native to prairies have returned."

How can ecologists study a population of organisms that they are trying to restore, like the bison, or one that may be causing problems, like the Nile perch or the zebra mussel? How can we know how many are in the population? With zebra mussels, one individual may not be a problem, but many might be. Instead of counting all of them, which would be impossible, scientists have ways of taking samples and using them to estimate population size.

In this activity, you will use a model of a transect to study the organisms found in two locations in a restored prairie. You will look for patterns among the components and consider how the information in the patterns can be useful to the scientists restoring the prairie.

Transects

One technique scientists can use to collect data on the number of organisms in a population, whether it is a species being restored or a species causing problems, is a transect. A **transect** is a specific path or area, often marked with a rope or measuring tape. Scientists mark the transect to show where data should be collected. The length of the transect and how often data are collected along the transect depends on what the scientists are studying. When scientists use transects in their work, they often say they are "conducting a transect." Ecologists often use a **quadrat**, a square or rectangular plot of land marked off, to determine where to collect their samples. In the photographs below, you can see scientists conducting transects in different environments.

Transect data can help scientists find relationships between a population of organisms and other components of an ecosystem. For example, if scientists are studying a population of purple coneflowers in a prairie, they may keep track of how much water is in the soil to look for patterns of soil moisture and how many coneflowers are growing.

GUIDING QUESTION

What patterns do you detect in the two environments, and how might the information in these patterns be useful to scientists?

MATERIALS

For each group of four students

      1 set of Transect 1 Cards

      1 set of Transect 2 Cards

      2 random number cubes

For each student

      1 Student Sheet 3.1, "Transect Results"

PROCEDURE

1. Look at the pictures below of the locations of the two prairie transects. What do you notice? Make a list of observations in your science notebook.

Prairie Transect 1

Prairie Transect 2

2. Read the information in the chart below. You will collect data on the four components of the environment listed.

Living and Nonliving Components of the Environment

LIVING	
Native plants	Plants naturally found in prairies, including purple coneflower, big bluestem, black-eyed Susan, and sandy milkweed
Non-native plants	Plants not naturally found in prairies, including smooth brome and Canada thistle
Grasshoppers	A native prairie insect that eats both native and non-native plants
NONLIVING	
Soil moisture	Can be dry, medium dry, or wet

3. Start with Prairie Transect 1.

4. Roll both random number cubes at the same time. Add the numbers on the cubes to determine your first data sampling point. Select ONLY the transect card for that data sampling point.

5. Read the transect card for your data sampling point aloud to your group. Record the data from that transect point on Student Sheet 3.1, "Transect Results."

6. Repeat Procedure Steps 4 and 5 two more times so you collect data from a total of three data sampling points.

7. Repeat Procedure Steps 4–6 for Prairie Transect 2.

8. With your group, discuss the differences you observed in Prairie Transects 1 and 2 based on the data you collected.

9. As a class, calculate the average number of native and non-native plants found in Prairie Transects 1 and 2. Also, note any differences in the soil moisture between the two locations. Discuss the differences you observed in the data you collected.

10. As a class, calculate the average number of grasshoppers found in the two prairie transects. Discuss why you think the scientists have started collecting data on the number of grasshoppers.

11. With your group, discuss what patterns you detected. What might be causing these patterns?

12. As a class, discuss what you would tell the scientists about their efforts to restore the prairies in these two different locations.

    • Are they on the right track?

    • Should they do anything differently in the future?

    • What other questions should the scientists ask themselves?

ANALYSIS

1. How did the samples vary across the groups in your class? Why do you think this is?

2. How did the average number of native plants, non-native plants, and grasshoppers differ in the two prairie locations?

3. a. When you compared the two prairie transects, what patterns did you detect?

    b. What factors or relationships might be the cause of these patterns?

4. Based on the data, does the current process for restoring the prairie seem to be working? Explain your reasoning.

4 Taking a Look Outside

FIELD STUDY

HOW WOULD YOU describe your local environment? For example, what kinds of organisms are common? What kinds of physical features are in the environment? Are there a lot of human-built structures? What kinds of patterns and relationships can you detect?

In this activity, you have the opportunity to investigate some of these questions by conducting a transect on your school grounds or another local area, as shown in the drawing below. Like ecologists, you will keep track of two kinds of components of an ecosystem. **Biotic** components are the living organisms in an environment, while **abiotic** components include all of the physical, nonliving components of the environment, including water, temperature and sunlight.

GUIDING QUESTION

What patterns do you observe when you investigate your own environment, and what might be causing these patterns?

MATERIALS

For each group of four students

    1 piece of string or rope at least 10 meters (m) long

    8 quadrat edges

    8 quadrat connectors

    1 magnifier

    1 thermometer

       flagging tape

PROCEDURE

1. As a class, work with your teacher to decide where you will conduct this transect. Think about locations you would like to learn more about and where you are most likely to observe interactions between biotic and abiotic components of the environment.

2. As a class, discuss why you are interested in the chosen location and what you would like to learn about. What initial questions do you have about this environment?

3. Brainstorm what kinds of organisms you expect to find at the location. Also consider what abiotic components you expect to find or that you want to measure.

4. Discuss what questions you want to try to answer with the data you collect.

5. As a class, decide how long to make your transects. A reasonable length would be between 10 m and 100 m, depending on the location you will sample. Also, decide on the distance between samples along your transect. For example, if your transect is 10 m long, you may decide to sample every meter, or if your transect is 100 m long, you may decide to sample every 10 m.

6. You will use the quadrat method for your transect. Assemble your quadrat as explained by your teacher.

7. Each group should cut a piece of string the length of the transect. Mark it at the distances you determined in Procedure Step 5 by tying a piece of flagging tape tightly around the string. As shown in the picture in the introduction, you will place your quadrat along the side of the string, with the flagging tape centered on one side of the quadrat.

8. Record your procedures for your investigation in your science notebook, and have your teacher approve them.

9. As a group, decide where you will place your transect. The transect line should cut straight across the environment you will be sampling.

10. Create a group data table in which to record patterns you find in your quadrat. Your table should contain rows for each quadrat sampling point and columns for each component you will investigate. Copy this data table into your science notebook.

11. At each quadrat sampling point, record everything you find or measure. Are you finding biotic or abiotic items? Be sure to look closely for living organisms—they may be under leaves or grass, or in cracks in the pavement.

12. Share your data with the whole class as instructed by your teacher.

13. In your group of four, discuss the following questions. Be prepared to share your ideas with the class.

   - What organisms did you observe?
   - What abiotic components did you observe?
   - Did you notice any patterns in where you found certain organisms?
   - What might cause these patterns?

14. As a class, based on your results so far, discuss what questions you have about your environment and how you would test those questions.

ANALYSIS

1. What was the most common biotic component in your group's transect?

2. What other biotic and abiotic components did you note?

3. Describe the relationships you see between the most common type of organism and other components of the environment.

4. What questions would you like to ask about the environment?

5. How would you test those questions?

5 A Suitable Habitat

LABORATORY

AN INVASIVE SPECIES is an introduced species that becomes successful in its new environment and causes or may cause problems there. Many introduced species do not become invasive because they cannot survive in the new environment. This is because all species require certain features for the places in which they can live. Think about different aquatic ecosystems, such as a small pond or a coral reef. While both of these environments contain water, they have very different characteristics. Coral reefs are found in oceans, which contain salt water, while most ponds are freshwater. An organism that lives in freshwater, like a zebra mussel, typically cannot survive in the coral reef environment because it does not have the right kinds of features, or adaptations, to survive in that other environment.

The specific kinds of biotic and abiotic requirements of a species determine in what kind of habitat it will be found. In the activity "Data Transects," you read about ecologists wanting to bring bison back to the restored prairie. Before they can do that, they need to make sure that the prairie has the biotic and abiotic components needed to make it a suitable habitat for the bison.

The photos below show a habitat for coral reef fishes and a garden habitat for butterflies.

In this activity, you will investigate a species' habitat requirements by looking at how individuals respond to different physical components in their environment. While ecologists often study what is happening to populations of organisms, like bison or zebra mussels, sometimes the answers come from examining the responses of individual organisms. The species you will study is the blackworm, *Lumbriculus variegatus*. Instead of going into the field to study this species, you will study it in the laboratory.

GUIDING QUESTION

How do the habitat requirements of individual organisms determine where a species will be found in nature?

SAFETY NOTE

Wash or sanitize your hands when you finish the investigation.

MATERIALS

For each group of four students

        5 blackworms (*Lumbriculus variegatus*)
        1 petri dish (100-millimeter [mm])
        1 pipette
        1 cup of treated tap water (or spring water)
        1 dropper
          sand
          aquarium gravel
          aquatic leaf litter (such as oak leaves in spring water)

PROCEDURE

Part A: Blackworms

1. Place five blackworms into a petri dish filled with treated tap water (or spring water).

2. Observe how the blackworms respond over the next few minutes. Discuss with your group any behaviors that seem to be common to most of the blackworms.

3. As a class, discuss what data to collect on the blackworms to determine which type(s) of material provide a good habitat for them.

4. Compare the materials available to you to create a blackworm habitat. Record any similarities and differences in the physical characteristics of the various habitat materials.

5. With your group, design an investigation to determine which type(s) of material provide a good blackworm habitat.

    When designing your investigation, think about the following questions:

    •   What is the purpose of your investigation?

    •   What variable are you testing?

    •   What variables will you keep the same?

    •   What is your initial idea based on your initial observations?

    •   How many trials will you conduct?

    •   Will you collect qualitative and/or quantitative data? How will these data help you to make a conclusion?

    •   How will you record these data?

6. Record your ideas and your planned procedure in your science notebook.

7. Make a data table in your science notebook that has space for all the data you need to record. You will fill it in during your experiment.

8. Obtain your teacher's approval of your investigation.

9. Conduct your investigation and record your results.

Part B: Reading

You have been investigating the blackworm's **habitat**, which is the location in an environment where an organism lives. Using sand, gravel, and leaf litter, you created a habitat. Then you observed black-worms interacting with that habitat. A group of blackworms living in the same habitat is known as a **population**. The total of all the areas where a species lives is its geographic **range**. In one habitat, there may be numerous populations of various species. For example, in a fresh-water pond, there might be populations of blackworms, snails, water plants, and fish.

All of the living and nonliving components, and all of the interactions among them, are known as an **ecosystem**. Anything that does not interact with the components is considered outside the boundary of that ecosystem. An ecosystem can be as small as a puddle or as large as planet Earth. An ecosystem that supports lots of types of organisms has a high biodiversity. **Biodiversity** is the variety of life at every level, from genes to species to ecosystems.

Ecosystems are constantly changing. Take, for example, the effects on the ecosystem if a pond fills with sediment from soil erosion. If resources decrease, the populations that depend on them decrease. A **resource** is any factor that can be consumed or used by an organism. In this case, a decrease of water in the pond means that aquatic animals and water plants would die. Even birds and insects that depend on the pond for food would disappear. Eventually, a new ecosystem would develop based on the grasses that would sprout from the new sediments.

Organisms have adaptive characteristics that help them to survive in a particular ecosystem. For instance, water is scarce in the desert. Cacti and other desert plants have thick, waxy surfaces that hold water inside. Animals have adaptive characteristics and behaviors as well. To avoid the heat, many desert animals hunt only at night.

This pond is filling with sediment and will eventually disappear. What will happen to the aquatic organisms that depend on the pond?

ANALYSIS

1. Based on your investigation, which type(s) of material provide a good habitat for blackworms? Explain how your results support your claim.

2. Based on what you now know about blackworms, in what type of environment do you think blackworms live? Explain your reasoning.

3. Adaptive features can include behaviors as well as other characteristics. What blackworm behaviors did you observe that might help it survive in its habitat?

4. What do you predict will happen if blackworms were introduced into a different ecosystem?

5. As you read in the activity "The Miracle Fish?" the government introduced Nile perch into Lake Victoria in the 1950s, but their population didn't start increasing until the 1970s. Based on what you learned in in this activity, suggest a reason for this observation.

   Hint: Think about the ecosystem and how it may have changed.

6 Ups and Downs

INVESTIGATION

As **YOU HAVE** learned, populations of organisms may change over time. They may also vary from one location to another. Scientists have extensively studied one species, zebra mussels, in many different locations and across a long period of time. As you read in in the activity "Introduced Species," zebra mussels were introduced from Europe and have caused a lot of problems in the United States. The mussel's success in freshwater environments has caused the loss of native wildlife as well as damaged boat hulls and motors, to which they latch on. How fast is this population spreading? Studying what has happened to populations of zebra mussels in European lakes, where they are native, can help scientists figure out what changes are occurring in the United States and what to expect for the future.

GUIDING QUESTION

Do zebra mussel populations change or stay the same in their native range?

Ecologists keep track of bison populations to make sure they are not decreasing in size.

Zebra mussel populations may become too large in some places.

MATERIALS

For each pair of students

    1 Student Sheet 6.1, "Ups and Downs"

PROCEDURE

Part A: Initial Observations

1. In your group of four, review the two tables below. Imagine that two different groups of ecologists used the quadrat method to collect data on the size of the zebra mussel population in Lake Miko, Poland, for two different time periods. (This lake is in the zebra mussel's native range.)

Zebra Mussel Population in Lake Miko, Period 1 (1959–1968)

YEAR	1959	1960	1962	1968
Number of zebra mussels (per m²)	2,211	95	93	97

Zebra Mussel Population in Lake Miko, Period 2 (1971–1976)

YEAR	1971	1972	1974	1976
Number of zebra mussels (per m²)	393	802	1,086	2,179

2. Divide your group in half. Assign one of the two data tables to each pair within your group.

3. With your partner, create a line graph of the data in your table using Student Sheet 6.1, "Ups and Downs." Remember, independent variables, such as time, are always graphed on the x-axis. Since you will compare graphs within your group, make sure that the x-axes of both graphs use the same scale.

4. After completing your graph, discuss with your partner what happens to the population of zebra mussels in Lake Miko from year to year.

Part B: A More Complete Analysis

5. Show your graph to the other students in your group. Point out the overall population trend—is the population increasing, decreasing, or stable?

6. Compare the two graphs. Discuss what conclusions you can make about the population trend in Lake Miko during Period 1 vs. Period 2.

7. Place the two graphs together, with the graph for Table 1 first and the graph for Table 2 second. If necessary, fold the edges of your sheets to fit the graphs together.

8. As a group, discuss what happens to the population trends when the two graphs are connected. How are the connected graphs different from each of the individual graphs? Be sure to

   • describe what happens to the population size of zebra mussels in Lake Miko from 1959–1976.

   • discuss whether you can make any definite conclusions about whether the population is increasing, decreasing, or staying the same.

ANALYSIS

1. Respond to the following items using the graph you created.

   a. Sketch a line on your graph predicting what will happen to the size of this population of zebra mussels during the 10 years after 1976.

   b. Why does the graph look that way? Support your claim with evidence and reasoning.

   c. What additional information would make you more confident in your prediction? Explain.

2. Consider population size when responding to the following items.

   a. What factors do you think affect the size of a population?

   b. Explain how each factor might affect population size: Would it cause the population to increase, decrease, or stay the same? Why?

3. Shown below are graphs of zebra mussel populations in three lakes near Lake Miko. Describe the population trend in each graph. How does each population change over time?

Zebra Mussel Populations in Three Lakes

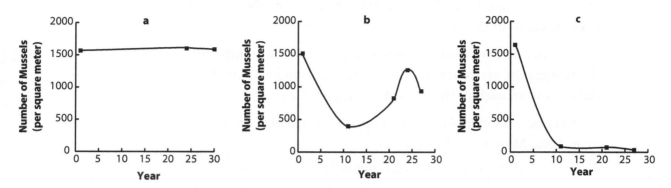

4. Shown below are the data collected from 1977 to 1987. How does this additional information compare with your response to Analysis item 1?

Zebra Mussel Population in Lake Miko, Period 3 (1977–1987)

YEAR	1977	1979	1982	1983	1987
Number of zebra mussels (per m²)	77	104	81	55	85

5. Zebra mussels were introduced into the United States in the late 1980s. They first appeared in Lake Erie, one of the Great Lakes shown in the map on the facing page. Today, the population of zebra mussels has reached as high as 70,000/m² in some parts of Lake Erie!

   a. How does this compare with the populations of zebra mussels found in the lakes in Poland?

   b. Why might zebra mussels be so much more abundant in their new environment in Lake Erie than in their native environment in Europe?

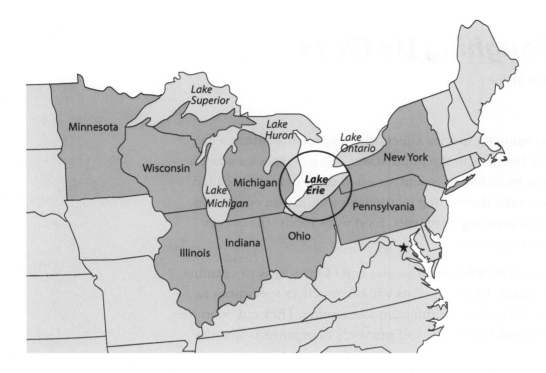

6. a. What do you predict has happened to the range of zebra
   mussels?

   b. Look at the data your teacher will show you. How well does
   your prediction match the actual data?

7 Coughing Up Clues

LABORATORY

HOW DO INTRODUCED species affect other organisms within a habitat? What happens to the populations of native species when a new organism is introduced? Scientists often draw diagrams, called **food webs**, to model the feeding relationships within an ecosystem. By showing what each organism eats, food webs model the energy relationships among species.

How can you find out what an organism eats? One way is to examine its stomach contents. Fish biologists will often collect specimens to take back to the laboratory or museum to examine. They cut open the stomach to determine the types and numbers of organisms that the fish have eaten.

But in the case of owls, you can also examine an owl pellet. An owl pellet is a combination of bones and fur that an owl coughs up, just as a cat coughs up a hairball. Owl pellets are formed when owls swallow their prey whole and their digestive system cannot break down fur and bones. Within 12 to 24 hours after eating, an owl coughs up a pellet. Piles of pellets are often found at the base of trees on which owls perch. These pellets help ecologists learn what and how much owls eat.

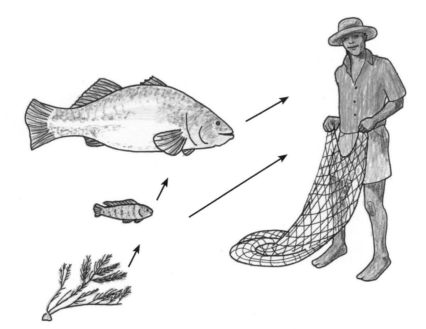

A simplified food web of Lake Victoria

Fish specimens in a museum

GUIDING QUESTION

What is an owl's place and role in a food web?

MATERIALS

For each group of four students

  1 owl pellet

For each student

  2 pointed wooden sticks

SAFETY NOTE

Wash or sanitize your hands when you finish the investigation.

PROCEDURE

1. One member of your group should carefully pull the owl pellet into four equal-sized pieces using the wooden sticks. Distribute one piece to each group member.

2. Use your pair of sticks to gently separate all of the bones from the fur of your piece of owl pellet.

3. Work with your group to divide all of the bones into groups based on their shapes. Use the table below, "Guide to Owl Pellet Bones," to help you.

Guide to Owl Pellet Bones

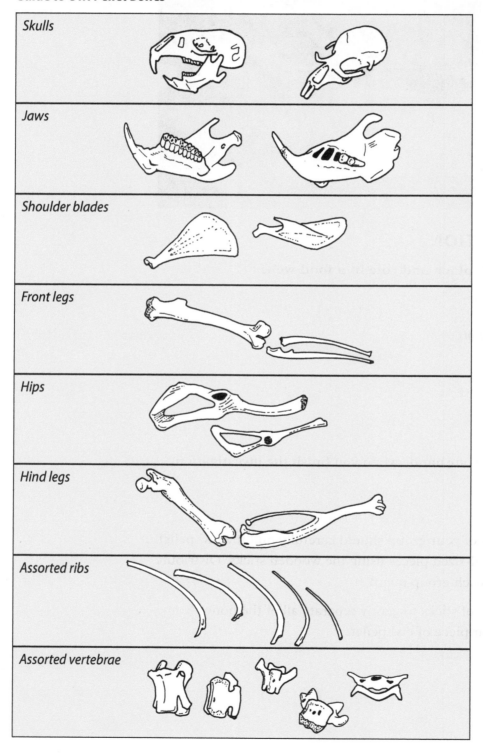

Skulls	
Jaws	
Shoulder blades	
Front legs	
Hips	
Hind legs	
Assorted ribs	
Assorted vertebrae	

4. Count and record the number of bones in each of your categories.

5. Try to arrange the bones to make a skeleton of one or more animals. Sketch your final arrangement(s).

ANALYSIS

1. What did you learn about the diet of owls from investigating an owl pellet? Include information about the type and number of organisms in an owl's diet. (Remember that an owl ejects a pellet within 12 to 24 hours after eating.)

2. Begin constructing an owl's food web. You will return to this food web in later activities.

   a. The organisms that you uncovered in your owl pellet are likely to be voles—small rodents similar to mice. Owls also eat other small mammals, such as shrews, and insects. Use this information about an owl's diet to develop a food web.

   b. Voles eat mostly plant material, such as grass, seeds, roots, and bark. Shrews eat insects. Add these relationships to your food web.

   c. Another kind of owl, the great horned owl, sometimes eats other owls. It also eats small mammals like voles. Add the great horned owl to your food web, and explain how it impacts the rest of the food web.

3. Consider your food web when responding to the following items:

   a. What would happen to the food web if a disease caused the populations of voles and shrews to die off? Explain your reasoning.

   b. How would this die-off affect the flow of energy in the ecosystem?

4. All living things have a place in a food web. What would your personal food web look like?

5. **Introduced Species Research Project**: Research the food web of the introduced species you are studying. What effects, if any, has your species had on native species? What effects do you predict it will have in the future?

EXTENSION

To identify the skulls you found in your owl pellet and learn more about owl pellets, visit the the SEPUP Third Edition Ecology page of the SEPUP website at *www.sepuplhs.org/middle/third-edition*, and go to the activity link.

8 *Eating for Matter and Energy*

READING

ONE IMPORTANT PART of every organism's habitat is its source of food. Food provides both the matter and energy organisms need to grow and reproduce. Understanding how matter and energy move in an ecosystem is a major goal of ecologists.

GUIDING QUESTION

How do matter and energy move in an ecosystem?

MATERIALS

For each group of four students

1 large sheet of paper
markers or colored pencils

READING

In the activity "Coughing Up Clues," you learned that the owls you investigated eat small mammals like voles and shrews. After the owl consumes the mammal, the owl's digestive system breaks down the mammal's matter into smaller pieces. Some of the matter is converted into other kinds of matter, including all the stuff the owl needs to build its body, including proteins, carbohydrates, and fats. As some of the matter is broken down, energy stored in the food is released. The food's released energy is needed by the owl's cells for life processes, including growth, movement, and reproduction.

You also learned that voles consume primarily plant material. The matter in the plants is broken down into different kinds of matter to build the vole's body, including its skeleton, muscles, and fur. The energy stored in the plants' molecules is used to allow the vole to breathe, search for more food, build tunnels, and produce offspring.

STOP TO THINK 1

Why are owls and voles called consumers?

Where do the plants that voles eat get their food? Unlike animals, plants make their own food instead of getting it from other organisms. They have special structures (chloroplasts) that allow them to use energy from the sun to convert some matter—carbon dioxide and water—into other kinds of matter—sugars and oxygen. This process is known as **photosynthesis**. The sugars that they produce through this process become their food. Some of the sugars are eventually used in chemical reactions that produce other kinds of matter, including the proteins, carbohydrates, and fats needed to build leaves, roots, and seeds. The rest of the sugar is used in chemical reactions that break the sugars down. The plants' process of breaking down the matter in food releases energy. In both plants and animals, the series of chemical reactions that breaks down sugars and releases energy is called **cellular respiration**.

STOP TO THINK 2

Why are plants called producers?

Because plants can store the food they make for later use, other types of organisms are able to take advantage of this stored food by eating the plants. In fact, voles consume only plants, getting nearly all of the matter and energy they need to survive and reproduce from them. The matter and energy stored in the plant's food is converted to matter and energy for use by the animal. However, some animals, like crows, eat both plants and other animals, getting matter and energy from both sources of food. Crows can live in numerous ecosystems, including that of owls.

STOP TO THINK 3

Return to your food web from Analysis item 2 in the activity "Coughing Up Clues." Add crows to the food web, and label each component of the food web as a consumer or producer. What kind of a relationship do crows have with owls?

Your food web is a model of the feeding relationships in an ecosystem. The arrows show the direction that energy and matter are moving within the ecosystem. When you drew an owl and a vole, and an arrow pointing from the vole to the owl, you were indicating the type of interaction between these two components in the ecosystem. The owl is a predator of the vole, and the vole is the prey of the owl. Both are consumers because neither makes its own food. When you added crows to your ecosystem, your model became more complex because crows get matter and energy from both plants and animals.

STOP TO THINK 4

Return to your food web model. Where does the energy come from to support plants making their own food?

Nearly every ecosystem on Earth today relies on the sun's energy as its initial energy source. Energy from the sun flows into ecosystems through plants, then into the animals that eat plants, and then into the animals that eat animals. Eventually, there is no more useable energy in the ecosystem. What happens to all of the energy?

Initially, plants absorb only 1% of the sun's energy. The rest of the sun's energy is released as heat. Of the solar energy that plants absorb, only 10% of it is stored in the plant. The remaining 90% flows out of the food web as heat energy, and the energy is no longer available to organisms. After the vole eats the plant, once again, 90% of the energy stored in the plant leaves the food web as heat energy and only 10% of it is transferred to the vole. This pattern continues until the top level of the food web is reached, when there is not enough energy stored to support any additional levels.

STOP TO THINK 5

Describe how energy flows into, through, and out of the owl's food web.

Where do plants get the matter they use to produce their own food? As you read earlier, through photosynthesis, plants combine carbon dioxide and water and rearrange the molecules to create sugar and oxygen. The water used in photosynthesis can come from any source, including rain water, ground water, surface water, and even moisture in the air. Aquatic plants are surrounded by water! The carbon dioxide that plants use is found in the air or is dissolved in water. It may seem strange to think that a gas we can't see or feel can be converted through a chemical process into an oak tree over 100 feet tall.

STOP TO THINK 6

Describe how matter moves throughout the owl's food web.

You may be asking yourself what happens to the matter after an organism dies, or when it reaches the top of the food web. We'll address this question in a later activity.

ANALYSIS

1. As a group, draw the owl's food web on a large sheet of paper, showing

   a. the components.

   b. how energy flows through the ecosystem.

   c. how matter moves through the ecosystem.

2. A volcano erupts 40 miles from the owl's ecosystem whose food web you drew. Ash from the eruption blocks sunlight over your ecosystem for several months.

   a. Explain what happens within the food web in the weeks that follow the eruption.

   b. The ash clears and several more months go by. What do you think will happen to your ecosystem?

3. Construct a model to show how energy flows into, through, and out of the owl's ecosystem. Your model must account for the fact that only 10% of the energy remains in the system from one level of the food web to the next. Your model may be a drawing, a physical model, or a mathematical model.

9 *Population Growth*

LABORATORY

THE ABILITY OF an organism to either make its own food, like plants, or acquire food from other organisms, like animals, is important in determining how successful that organism will be in its environment. In this activity, you will explore how the availability of food affects the growth of an entire population. The species you will study, *Paramecium caudatum*, is a single-celled organism that, like animals, consumes food made by other organisms.

Flamingos feeding

GUIDING QUESTION

How does the availability of food affect a population?

MATERIALS

For the class

- 1 culture of *Paramecium caudatum*
- 2 (or more) clear plastic cups
- 1 packet of wheat seeds
- 2 (or more) droppers

For each pair of students

- 2 microscope slides
- 2 coverslips
- 1 microscope
- 1 paper towel

SAFETY NOTE

Wash or sanitize your hands when you finish the investigation.

PROCEDURE

Part A: Observing *Paramecium*

1. Review the rules for handling a microscope on the following page.

Parts of a Microscope

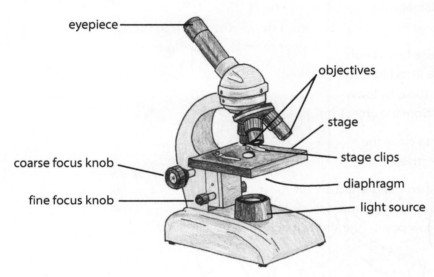

2. As instructed by your teacher, use the dropper in the cup containing the *Paramecium* to place a drop of liquid from that cup on your slide.

3. Carefully touch one edge of the coverslip, at an angle, to the liquid on your slide (as shown below). Slowly allow the coverslip to drop into place.

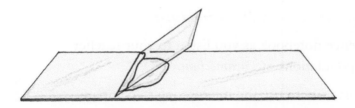

4. Be sure that your microscope is set on the lowest power (shortest objective) before placing your slide onto the microscope's stage. Center the slide so that the specimen is directly over the light opening, and adjust the microscope settings as necessary.

Rules for Handling a Microscope

- Always carry a microscope using two hands, as shown in the picture to the right.

- Rotate the objectives carefully. Do not allow them to touch the stage or anything placed on the stage, such as a slide. This can damage the microscope.

- When using the coarse focus knob, begin with the stage in its highest position and always focus by lowering the stage (away from the objective).

- Use only lens paper to clean the eyepiece or the objectives.

- When you have finished using a microscope, remember to turn off the microscope light and set the microscope back to low power (the shortest objective, usually 4×).

5. Begin by observing the sample on low power. You may need to search the slide for *Paramecium* organisms. If you wish to switch to medium power, do so without moving the slide. Adjust the microscope setting as needed.

6. Try to focus on one individual organism and observe it for a while, noting how it moves and takes in food items.

Part B: Comparing Populations of *Paramecium*

7. Take notes in your science notebook as you listen to your teacher describe the different populations of *Paramecium*.

8. You will have the opportunity to use the microscope to compare these different populations. Before doing so, do you predict there will be any differences? If not, explain your scientific reasoning. If so, how do you predict these populations will differ? Explain your scientific reasoning.

9. As instructed by your teacher, collect samples from the different populations and observe them under the microscope.

10. Record your observations as instructed by your teacher.

ANALYSIS

1. Construct a food web for your *Paramecium* ecosystem. Be sure to label the components and illustrate how they interact. Indicate how matter and energy move into, through, and out of the ecosystem.

2. Did your findings support or refute your prediction in Procedure Step 8? Explain your answer using your evidence.

3. Explain how food availability affected the populations of *Paramecium*. Be sure to use your data to develop your explanation.

4. Predict whether the *Paramecium* populations will continue to grow. Justify your prediction with scientific reasoning.

5. How could you design an experiment to test your ideas?

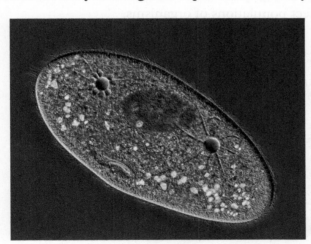

Paramecium *as seen through a microscope*

10 *Interactions in Ecosystems*

INVESTIGATION

IN THE PREVIOUS activity, you looked at how the availability of food affected the population size of *Paramecium* in the laboratory. Organisms in a natural ecosystem interact with many biotic and abiotic components in the environment. For example, the number of squirrels living in and near a city park might rise or fall because of biotic factors, such as the availability of nuts, seeds, and berries; the number of people who feed them; and the presence of raccoons and hawks. Abiotic factors, such as water shortages, mild or extreme weather, expansion of the parkland, or construction of homes in the area, might also affect the population size of squirrels.

The types of interactions between two species in an ecosystem may be helpful or harmful to one or both of the species. The interaction may also have no impact at all. In this activity, you will explore how different kinds of interactions in an ecosystem affect populations of organisms.

Impalas with oxpeckers on their backs

GUIDING QUESTION

How do interactions with living or nonliving factors in eco-systems affect populations?

MATERIALS

For each student

1 Student Sheet 10.1, "Patterns of Interactions"
1 Student Sheet 10.2, "Types of Biotic Interactions"

PROCEDURE

1. Read the six scenarios described below. Each one describes an interaction between a population and an abiotic or biotic factor.

Scenario 1: Freshwater Lake Fish

Rainbow smelt can survive in a wide range of lake environments. When rainbow smelt were introduced to Crystal Lake in Northern Wiscon-sin, they quickly changed the ecosystem of the lake. For example, they ate up much of the food preferred by other fish. They have nearly elimi-nated the yellow perch, another type of fish.

Scenario 2: Marine Worms and Ocean Temperatures

A kind of scale worm lives on sea stars in shal-low ocean waters in the Pacific Northwest. The worm population increases when water temperatures drop in winter, and then drops as water temperatures rise through the summer.

Scenario 3: Insects in Fields and Orchards

Insects are a pest in crop fields, orchards, and other farmland. Evidence suggests that the introduction of a parasitic wasp can cause the levels of certain insect pests in farm fields to decline.

Scenario 4: Phosphorus and Algae Growth

Phosphorus is an essential nutrient for plants and algae. When phosphorus levels in water rise due to the presence of sewage waste, the population of algae increases.

Scenario 5: Canadian Lynx and Snowshoe Hare

The Canada lynx is a member of the cat family, not much larger than a house cat. In Northern Canada, the lynx's preferred diet is the snow-shoe hare. When the snowshoe hare population decreases, the lynx kittens are often unable to survive.

Scenario 6: Oxygen and Fish Populations

Investigations of a fish population in a lake showed that it was able to survive some decrease in oxygen. But as oxygen levels con-tinued to drop, the fish population decreased rapidly.

2. Work with your group to examine the patterns of interaction illustrated by the graphs on Student Sheet 10.1, "Patterns of Interaction." Describe what is happening to each line on the graph and how it relates to the other line.

3. Work together to match each scenario to one or more graphs. Record the graph(s) that match the scenario.

4. If the interaction is biotic, discuss with your group if the interaction is helpful, harmful, or neutral to one or both species. Use Student Sheet 10.2, "Types of Biotic Interactions," to determine which pattern of biotic interaction best fits with each pattern.

5. With your group, discuss what you think might happen to the organisms on each graph over time.

6. Your teacher will assign your group one of the scenarios to focus on. Explain to the rest of the class why you think the graph you selected matches the scenario.

7. Work individually to write your explanation for your scenario as instructed by your teacher.

ANALYSIS

1. Identify each of the following as one of the types of biotic interactions:

   a. Mountain lions eat deer.

   b. Lice live on a person's head.

   c. Hummingbirds feed on plant nectar.

   d. Ladybugs eat aphids.

   e. Deer and elk browse for shrubs in winter.

   f. Vultures eat the remains of an animal killed by a mountain lion.

   g. Roundworms live in the intestines of dogs.

   h. Gophers dig tunnels and expose insects to nearby birds.

   i. Bees gather nectar and pollinate flowers.

   j. Oxpeckers eat ticks off the backs of impalas.

2. Look back at your owl food web to respond to the following:

   a. What patterns of interactions are in the food web?

   b. Are any types of biotic interactions missing? If so, what might be some likely examples that you could add to the food web?

3. Give an example of how humans interact with another species in each of the following ways:

   a. predator–prey

   b. competition

   c. mutualism

4. **Introduced Species Research Project**: Research and describe how the introduced species you are studying interacts with other components in the environment.

EXTENSION

Use the computer simulation linked on the SEPUP Third Edition Ecology page of the SEPUP website at *www.sepuplhs.org/middle/third-edition* to examine predator–prey relationships and competitive relationships in greater depth. This simulation allows you to add and remove producers and consumers from the ecosystems. Make predictions about how removing one species will affect the remaining species. What will happen if you add a species? Does it matter it the species is a producer? a consumer? prey? predator?

11 *Cycling of Matter*

LABORATORY

IN THE ACTIVITY, Eating for Matter and Energy," you learned how energy flows into, through, and out of an ecosystem. But how does matter move in an ecosystem? To answer this question, you will investigate another important biotic component in ecosystems known as decomposers. You know that producers make their own food, and consumers use food made by other organisms. What role do decomposers play in an ecosystem? What types of organisms are decomposers?

Organisms that eat dead organisms and wastes from living organisms are known as **decomposers.** Worms, bacteria, and fungi are decomposers. You can think of decomposers as a special type of consumer—one that eats dead organisms and waste material.

Fungi, such as these mushrooms, decompose wood and other dead plant material.

Decomposers, like worms and bacteria, can seem unimportant because they are so small and can be overlooked or invisible to us. But decomposers break down the large molecules in the dead and decaying materials that they feed upon and release smaller molecules back into the physical environment. These smaller molecules contain carbon, nitrogen, and phosphorous, which can then be used by producers to make their own food. In this way, matter is recycled within the ecosystem.

Without decomposers, dead organisms would pile up and the nutrients they contain could not be re-used by plants. Eventually, the fertility of soil and aquatic ecosystems would be reduced to nothing. Imagine what the bottom of a lake would look like without any decomposers!

In this activity, you will examine soil samples to look for decomposers and for evidence of decomposition.

GUIDING QUESTION

What is the role of decomposers in the cycling of matter in an ecosystem?

MATERIALS

For each group of four students

    1 soil sample

    1 stand

    1 funnel

    1 perforated disc

    1 clamp

    1 piece of tubing

    1 large piece of rectangular filter paper

    1 petri dish

    1 cup of water

       markers

For each pair of students

    1 microscope

    1 microscope slide

    1 coverslip

    1 dropper

SAFETY NOTE

Wash or sanitize your hands when you finish the investigation.

PROCEDURE

Part A: Investigating Soil

1. Obtain 1/2 cup of soil as instructed by your teacher.

2. Start building your nematode extractor by placing the tubing on the spout of the funnel. Then attach the clamp onto the middle of the tubing, as shown at left. Make sure that the tubing is pushed as far as it can go into the clamp; otherwise, the water can drip out.

3. Place the funnel in the stand and the perforated disc into the funnel.

4. Add water to the funnel to the level of the perforated disc.

5. Put a single layer of the rectangular filter paper in the funnel. You may need to separate the layers. Add a layer of your soil sample, no more than 1 cm deep, onto the filter paper.

6. Fold the filter paper over the soil. Add just enough water to cover the soil and filter paper. Set aside for 1 day.

Nematode extractor

Part B: Investigating Decomposition

7. Listen and observe as your teacher sets up the device for following decomposition over time.

8. As a class, discuss what you expect to happen over time, and establish a method for keeping track of your findings.

Part C: Searching for Nematodes

9. Carefully remove the clamp to release a small amount (less than 5 mL) of water into the petri dish. Share this sample in your group of four.

10. You might be able to see some small, white thread-like objects in the water. Try to suck up one of the thread-like objects into the dropper, and then squeeze a couple of drops from the dropper onto a microscope slide.

11. Carefully touch one edge of the coverslip, at an angle, to the mixture. Slowly allow the coverslip to drop into place.

12. Begin by observing the slide on low power (usually the 4X objective). Be sure that the sample is in the center of the field of view (you may need to move the slide slightly) and completely in focus before going on to the next step.

    Hint: To check that you are focused on the sample, move the slide slightly while you look through the eyepiece—the sample that you are focused on should move as you move the slide.

13. Without moving the slide, switch to medium power (usually the 10X objective). Adjust the microscope settings as necessary.

    Hint: If material on the slide is too dark to see, increase the amount of light on the slide by slightly opening the diaphragm under the stage.

14. While looking through the eyepiece, move the slide around slowly so that you see all parts of your sample. As you scan the slide, look for movement, especially of thin, colorless organisms like the ones shown in the photo below. These organisms look like small earthworms but are actually members of a different phylum. These tiny worms are called nematodes (NEM-uh-toads). (If you do not find any nematodes on your slide, make another slide from your sample.)

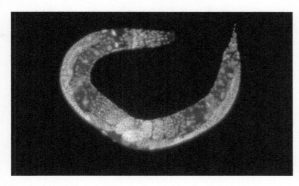

A nematode

15. Try to count the number of nematodes on your slide. Compare the number of nematodes you and your partner find with the rest of your group.

16. When you have completed your observations, turn off the microscope light and set the microscope back to low power.

ANALYSIS

1. Use the food web that you began in the "Coughing Up Clues" activity to respond to the following:

   a. Which of the organisms in this ecosystem are producers? Which are consumers?

   b. Which are decomposers? If your food web does not already include decomposers, add them to the ecosystem.

   c. Add arrows to show how matter cycles in the system.

2. Imagine that something kills most of the bacteria and other decomposers in a lake. What would happen to the cycling of matter in the ecosystem?

3. True or false: The amount of matter in a living system stays the same. Explain your thinking.

12 Modeling the Introduction of a New Species

MODELING

WHAT HAPPENS WHEN a new species is introduced into an ecosystem? Does it change the availability of food and, therefore, the matter and energy available to other organisms?

Consider the zebra mussel. As you know by now, this species has been causing many problems in the United States since humans unintentionally introduced it in the 1980s. How can such a tiny organism, which averages around an inch long, cause such serious problems?

To answer this question, we need to look at how a zebra mussel gets its food. Like all animals, zebra mussels acquire their food by eating other organisms. They feed by filtering microscopic plants and animals out of the water. A one-inch zebra mussel can filter 1 L of water a day. If you had a number of zebra mussels that totaled 1 kg of mass, they could filter 180 L each day. That's the equivalent of a 45-kg (100 pound) person filtering 8,100 L per day. (Imagine over 4,000 2-L bottles!) Zebra mussels are so efficient at filtering out food from the environment that other animals that feed the same way can't compete with them.

Zebra mussels feeding

In this activity, you will model what happens to matter and energy when a new species is introduced into an ecosystem.

GUIDING QUESTION

How does a new species affect the flow of energy and cycling of matter through an ecosystem?

MATERIALS

For each group of four students

    1 set of 9 Food Web Cards

PROCEDURE

Part A: Constructing your Food Web

1. Work with your group to examine all nine of the Food Web Cards in your set.

2. As a group, choose at least four cards and construct a simple food chain. Record your food chain in your science notebook.

3. Identify the producers and consumers, and show how energy flows and matter cycles through the ecosystem.

4. Work with your group to create a food web using all of the cards in your set, identifying what happens to energy and matter for each interaction. Record your food web in your science notebook.

5. Discuss your work with another group of students with the same set of Food Web Cards. How similar or different are your ideas?

6. Look at the food webs created by groups that have a different set of Food Web Cards, and make note of any similarities and differences.

Part B: Introducing a Species to your Food Web

7. Your teacher will give you a new species to add to your food web. Identify what type of organism it is and its role in the ecosystem.

8. Use your model to explore how this new species affects the flow of energy and cycling of matter through your ecosystem, and record your revised food web in your science notebook.

9. As instructed by your teacher, share and discuss your new model with another group.

ANALYSIS

1. Explain how the introduction of your new species affected your ecosystem. Be sure to address which interactions were affected.

2. What would happen if

   a. the top predators disappeared from your ecosystem? This might happen if the predators were overhunted. How does this affect the flow of energy through your ecosystem?

   b. the producers disappeared from your ecosystem? This might happen if a disease caused the producers to die off. How does this affect the flow of energy through your ecosystem?

3. **Introduced Species Research Projec**t: Explain how the introduction of the species you are investigating impacts the flow of energy and cycling of matter in the ecosystem.

13 Abiotic Impacts on Ecosystems

INVESTIGATION

ECOSYSTEMS ARE ALWAYS changing. For example, the type and number of organisms may change or the amount of available water may change. Sometimes an ecosystem changes back and forth within a small range. Such an ecosystem is considered **stable**. At other times, biotic or abiotic factors undergo major changes, or **disruptions**, and the ecosystem is no longer stable.

GUIDING QUESTION

How can abiotic disruptions, such as fire, affect the flow of energy and cycling of matter in an ecosystem?

MATERIALS

For each group of four students

- 1 set of 6 Forest Change Cards
- 1 set of 6 Forest Change Caption Cards

For each student

- 1 Student Sheet 13.1, "Energy Changes in a Forest Ecosystem"

PROCEDURE

1. Carefully examine the six Forest Change Cards. With your group, use words to identify or describe the plants and animals on the cards.

2. The Forest Change Cards show changes in a forest ecosystem. Discuss how the drawings are similar to and different from a real forest ecosystem.

3. Which card shows a forest ecosystem that has existed for a long time? Place it as the first card in your timeline.

A landslide is one type of abiotic disruption.

4. Determine what happened in this forest over time. Place the remaining five cards in the order you think they happened, from oldest to most recent. Record your sequence on Student Sheet 13.1, "Energy Changes in a Forest Ecosystem."

5. Use the information on each card to complete an energy pyramid on Student Sheet 13.1 for the ecosystem at the time shown on the card.

   • Be sure to draw in the original source of energy for each pyramid.

   • If there are levels of a pyramid that did not contain living organisms at that time, write "none."

6. Your teacher will hand out a series of six Forest Change Caption Cards. Read each caption carefully, and match it to the appropriate event on Student Sheet 13.1.

7. Read the paragraph below about the role of fire in an ecosystem.

Fire in Ecosystems

While fires can be very destructive when they occur where people live, fires caused by lightning regularly occur in some ecosystems, including prairies and forests. By burning dry plant material, fire acts as a decomposer. The energy in the fire converts the large molecules stored in plants to small molecules that return to the soil or air. In some areas with poor soil, fire actually increases the productivity of the soil by returning substances to the soil that organisms need to grow and reproduce. Because fires are so common in some ecosystems, some plants and animals have adaptations that allow them to succeed in an area that has recently had a fire. These are called fire-adapted species. Some trees have very thick bark to insulate against fire and lose their lower branches as they grow. Some plants have their growing point underground so that if a fire destroys the parts of the plant above ground, it can still survive. Some plants have seeds that will only start growing after a fire.

ANALYSIS

1. Explain how fire helps matter cycle through the biotic and abiotic parts of an ecosystem.

2. Compare and contrast how the cycling of matter and the flow of energy within an ecosystem change when there is

   a. an abrupt ecosystem change, like a fire.

   b. an ecosystem change that occurs over time, like a drought.

3. Explain why owls take longer to return to a forest ecosystem after a fire than do plants or voles.

4. Should fires caused by lightning in forests or prairies be put out or left to burn? Explain your thinking.

5. What are some types of human-caused disruptions in the ecosystems around you?

14 | *Effects of an Introduced Species*

INVESTIGATION

As you know by now, introduced species are a major type of biotic disruption. When scientists realized that zebra mussels were likely to find their way into the Hudson River—a river that runs through the state of New York and drains into the Atlantic Ocean—those scientists were in a unique position to understand and document the impact of the invasion.

Scientists don't usually have data about an ecosystem until after the new species appears. However, scientists began collecting data on the Hudson River's ecosystem in 1986. They decided to study the whole Hudson River ecosystem over a 200-km stretch.

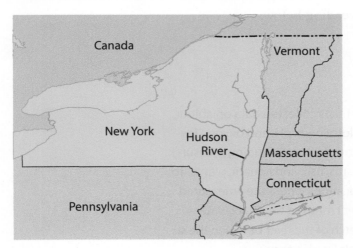

Map of the Hudson River

Ecosystems are usually not isolated—what happens in one place may have an effect on a place that seems far away. The scientists decided to do a long-term study because ecosystems are dynamic—they are constantly changing for many reasons. Some reasons for change are natural disturbances, and others are human-caused disturbances. Disturbances can affect many interactions between biotic and abiotic factors in the ecosystem.

In this activity, you will compare data collected by scientists in the years before and after the arrival of the zebra mussels. From the data, you will begin to build a picture of how the ecosystem has changed.

GUIDING QUESTION

What do the scientific data tell you about how the Hudson River has changed after the introduction of the zebra mussel?

MATERIALS

For each pair of students

    1 computer with Internet access

PROCEDURE

1. With your class, watch the video clips, *The Problem* and *Observation*.

2. With your partner, complete the reading below.

Collecting Data

To study the Hudson River ecosystem, scientists collected data on abiotic factors, such as the water's temperature, cloudiness, pH, and oxygen levels. The scientists also collected data on biotic factors, including measuring the populations of microscopic organisms, fish, and aquatic plants. To study the whole river, they chose six key locations where they measured several variables. They also used the transect method to collect water samples every 2–4 km along a 170-km stretch of the river between the six key locations. At that time, no zebra mussels lived in the river.

In May 1991, a few years after they were first found in the Great Lakes, zebra mussels appeared in the Hudson River. Based on what scientists already knew about the Hudson's water chemistry, its river bottom, and other conditions, they predicted that zebra mussels would invade the river. Within a year, scientists estimated that the zebra mussel population had reached 500 billion! If you had a huge balance scale and put the Hudson River zebra mussels on one side, they would outweigh all the other consumers in the ecosystem combined—all the fish, zooplankton, worms, shellfish, and bacteria.

3. Now you will help scientists figure out how the zebra mussels have affected the river ecosystem. With your partner, use the table below to choose three factors to investigate. Be sure to choose factors you think zebra mussels might affect.

Biotic factors		Abiotic factors
	Phytoplankton: *These tiny drifting organisms use photosynthesis to make food. Scientists filter plankton from the water and measure the amount of chlorophyll they contain to estimate the amount of phytoplankton.* (**Graph Parameter:** *Chlorophyll a*)	**Water Temperature:** *Temperature affects an organism's metabolism—the internal chemical reactions that affect its health and growth.* (**Graph Parameter:** *Temperature*)
	Zooplankton: *These tiny animals drift in open water, feeding on phytoplankton. Scientists measure their abundance by filtering river water through mesh nets.* (**Graph Parameters:** *Rotifers, copepods, Cladocera*)	**Dissolved Oxygen:** *Oxygen dissolves in water. Both producers and consumers (like zebra mussels) take up oxygen during respiration. Producers also give off oxygen.* (**Graph Parameter:** *Dissolved oxygen*)
	Freshwater Mollusks: *Mollusks, such as clams, mussels, and oysters, feed by filtering food. Native mollusks in the Hudson River include Unionidae and Sphaeriidae, which eat bacteria and phytoplankton.* (**Graph Parameters:** *Unionidae, Sphaeriidae*)	**Water Clarity:** *Scientists use a Secchi disk to measure how clear water is. They lower the disk into the water until they can no longer see the pattern on the disk's surface. The clearer the water, the greater the depth at which scientists can see the pattern.* (**Graph Parameter:** *Secchi depth*)
	Watershed Nutrients from Organic Matter: *Organic particles from soil, dead leaves, and other materials wash into the river from the watershed (the land around the river). This organic matter feeds many organisms, especially bacteria.* (**Graph Parameters:** *Bacterial abundance, bacterial production*)	**Suspended Solids:** *The solid particles suspended in water affect its clarity and quality. These particles can be both biotic (like phytoplankton) and abiotic (like silt and clay). Zebra mussels consume huge amounts of biotic suspended solids, clearing large bodies of water.* (**Graph Parameter:** *Total suspended solids*)
	Fish: *Fish eat zooplankton, invertebrates, or other fish.* (**Graph Parameters:** *Alosa (pelagic fish), Centrarchidae (littoral fish)*)	

4. Following your teacher's directions, develop a testable question and a prediction for how each factor you selected will change after the zebra mussel's arrival in the river. Write down why you chose these factors and your prediction for each factor. Have your teacher approve your choice of factors.

5. With your partner, go to the link on the Ecology page of the SEPUP website as instructed by your teacher. Select "Graph the Data."

6. You will examine data from the Kingston location. Select "Over Time," and use the map to choose the Kingston location.

7. Set the first parameter to "Zebra mussel," and set the second parameter to one of the factors that you chose in Procedure Step 3.

8. Examine the graph prior to the arrival of the zebra mussel in 1991 and afterwards, and record your findings in your science notebook.

9. Repeat this process for each of the other two factors you chose.

ANALYSIS

1. For each factor you examined, do the data show stability or change in the Hudson River ecosystem? Support your claim with evidence and reasoning.

2. In Procedure Step 4, you made predictions about how each of the three factors would be affected by the introduction of the zebra mussel. Describe whether the data supported your predictions.

3. How did the introduction of the zebra mussel change the Hudson River ecosystem?

4. Your observations covered data that spanned from a few years before to over 20 years after the zebra mussel arrived in the Hudson River. Predict what the data might show in the next 20 years. Explain the reasons for your prediction.

15 Too Many Mussels

TALKING IT OVER

ZEBRA MUSSELS CAUSE major problems for both people and other organisms. They clog water pipes that people depend on for drinking water—as many as 750,000 zebra mussels have been found in 1 m² of pipe! Zebra mussels outcompete other organisms for food, causing these other species to decline. They also spread the bacteria that cause botulism to birds that eat them. Botulism can be fatal to both birds and humans. Zebra mussels cost the United States billions of dollars each year because of the damage they cause and our efforts to control them.

How did the zebra mussel get to U.S. and Canadian waterways, including rivers and lakes? Scientists agree that its arrival was due to the dumping of ballast water by large ships coming from Europe. Ballast water is used to keep ships stable in the water. European ships take on ballast water that is full of zebra mussels, and those zebra mussels are then released when the ships dump the ballast water. The zebra mussel has been able to spread all across the United States because waterways are connected either naturally or artificially through human-made canals. Boats or trailers that are moved from one waterway to another can also spread zebra mussels.

What can humans do to reduce or eliminate the problems caused by the zebra mussel? In this activity, you will explore some possible solutions to these problems.

GUIDING QUESTION

How can humans control or eliminate an invasive species?

In this photo, you can see zebra mussel shells pile along the beach in a stack more than a foot high.

MATERIALS

For each student

　1　Student Sheet 15.1, "Trade-offs of Zebra Mussel Control Methods"

　1　Student Sheet 15.2, "Designing a Possible Solution to a Specific Zebra Mussel Problem"

PROCEDURE

Part A: Trade-offs of Zebra Mussel Control Methods

1. As a class, read "Designing Solutions to Environmental Problems."

> ## Designing Solutions to Environmental Problems
>
> Engineers design solutions to problems. However, the aim of engineering is not just to design a solution but to design the best solution. Before designing a solution, engineers will identify criteria and constraints. **Criteria** are the desired goals and the desired features of the solution. **Constraints** are something that limit the solution to the problem.
>
> Recall the prairie restoration project that you learned about in an earlier activity. One criterion for that project might be that the prairie must sustain a herd of at least 20 bison. A constraint might be that the prairie cannot be made any larger because of the housing development surrounding it. Designing, or deciding on, the best solution often requires making trade-offs between criteria. With the prairie, it may be possible to sustain 20 bison but only if supplemental food is provided for the bison. The money spent to purchase the food may result in fewer educational programs offered by the prairie's nature center.

2. With your group, read and discuss the following descriptions about various zebra mussel control methods that scientists and engineers have used or considered.

   • Use Student Sheet 15.1, "Trade-offs of Zebra Mussel Control Methods," to identify the advantages and disadvantages of the different methods.

   • Be sure to make note of the situations where each method might be beneficial or harmful.

Zebra Mussel Control Methods

Chemical Control

Chlorine: Chlorine added to water containing zebra mussels is an effective way to kill them. Some studies have shown that nearly 100% of zebra mussels die when chlorine is added to the water for at least two weeks. However, chlorine will kill most other organisms in the water, including native species. When chlorine is mixed with certain mussel proteins, cancer-causing substances may form, which are dangerous to the environment and human health.

Potassium chloride: Many poisons are not effective on zebra mussels because they will close their shells and stop feeding once they detect a poison. However, by coating the poisonous potassium chloride with vegetable oil, zebra mussels mistake these particles as food and consume them. In a controlled environment, 60% of mussels died when exposed to the coated poison. However, the effectiveness of this control method still needs to be tested in the natural environment, and the effects on other species are not known.

Mechanical Control

Manual removal: Zebra mussels can be removed from hard surfaces, especially from inside water pipes, using a high-pressure washer or other scraping technique. Manual removal is not known to cause harm to other species. However, this method requires a large effort by people, which is expensive. It is also possible for the mussels to come back in a year. The tiny larvae of the mussels live in the open water separate from the adult zebra mussel clusters, and so are not removed by this manual method.

Screening: Filtering water through a screen is another way to mechanically remove zebra mussels from water pipes. Engineers have developed a filter than can screen out even the smallest zebra mussel larvae (0.1 mm). In a trial, no adult zebra mussel successfully moved through the filter. Of the small number of eggs and larvae that slipped through the screen, all were dead or dying. The cost of using this filter has not yet been determined nor has it been considered for use in natural ecosystems.

A worker uses a power washer to remove mussels from inside a water pipe.

Zebra Mussel Control Methods *continued*

Biological Control

Bacteria: Although phytoplankton are their preferred food, zebra mussels can filter out and consume bacteria as a food source. When scientists introduce a certain kind of bacteria (*Pseudomonas fluorescens*) into the environment at high densities, a toxin within these bacterial cells destroys the mussel's digestive system. These bacteria kill 75–100% of zebra mussels in experiments, and they do not seem to affect other species in the laboratory. While *P. fluorescens* is an unusual cause of disease in humans, it can occur.

Predation: Zebra mussels do not have many natural predators in North America, but in their native range, over 175 species of birds and fish are known to prey upon them. In European lakes, diving ducks thrive on zebra mussels and have the potential to reduce the zebra mussel population by over 50%. Small pieces of zebra mussels have been found in the stomachs of many species of fish in the United States, but so far no predator is known to successfully control zebra mussels. However, scientists are beginning to research predation by a natural predator as a method of control. Scientists say that research should focus on species that favor zebra mussels over other prey.

A ruddy duck is a type of diving duck.

Hint: Compare and contrast the problems the zebra mussel causes for

- humans because of the disruption of ecosystem services, like access to fresh water.

- native organisms in the ecosystem.

Part B: Identifying a Possible Solution to a Zebra Mussel Problem

3. Listen as your teacher assigns your group one of the following two design tasks, both addressing problems caused by zebra mussels:

- problems affecting humans

- problems affecting native organisms

4. Use Student Sheet 15.2, "Designing a Possible Solution to a Specific Zebra Mussel Problem," to design your group's best solution. You may choose several of the proposed control methods to implement. Make sure to provide your reasoning to justify why you think a solution or combination of solutions is the best choice. You must specify the criteria and constraints of your solution.

5. Meet with another group that was assigned the same problem and share your solution. Be sure to discuss the criteria and constraints for your solutions.

6. Within your groups, make any revisions to your solution based on what you learned from other groups. You may also revise your criteria and constraints.

7. As a class, compare and contrast the best solution(s) for solving the two kinds of zebra mussel problems—those affecting human and those affecting native organisms.

ANALYSIS

1a. Evaluate the different zebra mussel control methods for the problem you were trying to solve. Which method(s) are most effective? Be sure to state your claim, provide evidence to support your claim, and provide the scientific reasoning for why your evidence supports your claim.

1b. Considering all of the problems caused by zebra mussels for both people and biodiversity, which control method is the best, taking into account environmental needs, economic needs and social needs?

Hint: To write a complete answer, first state your opinion. Provide two or more pieces of evidence that support your opinion. Then consider all sides of the issue, and identify the trade-offs of your decision.

2. Scientific knowledge is valuable when making decisions because it can describe the consequences of actions. However, science is not usually the only consideration when making a decision. Give an example of a problem that affects your own community, and explain what needs to be considered when solving the problem.

3. **Introduced Species Research Project**: How does the introduced species you are investigating disrupt the ecosystem services that humans derive from the environment?

16 *Presenting the Facts*

PROJECT

INTRODUCED SPECIES CAN have an enormous impact on the economy as well as on native ecosystems. Your research project and your study of ecology have helped you to become an expert on one introduced species. Why are some introduced species more likely to be successful than others, and how do those species affect the biotic and abiotic components of the ecosystem?

GUIDING QUESTIONS

What effect can certain introduced species have on an environment? What, if anything, can or should humans do to control these species?

MATERIALS

1 Student Sheet 16.1, "Anticipation Guide: Introduced Species"

PROCEDURE

1. In the "Introduced Species" activity, you began a research project on an introduced species. You will now present your research to the class. Use Student Sheet 2.1, "Introduced Species Research," as you plan your presentation. Your presentation should help your audience understand how this species impacts the ecosystem. It should also help the audience make an informed decision about what, if anything, should be done to control this introduced species.

   a. When planning your presentation, keep the following in mind:

      • All the members of your group must participate.

      • Since any group member may be asked to answer questions from the class, all group members should fully understand the report.

      • Your presentation time is limited.

      • Many people learn best from a mix of visual, written, and spoken information. Include graphs and maps when possible.

   b. When listening to other groups,

      • pay close attention because, as a class, you will need to compare and contrast all of the introduced species.

      • ask clarifying questions or take notes if there is something you want to mention during the class discussion that will follow all of the presentations.

2. After all of the presentations, as a class, follow your teacher's directions for comparing and contrasting how each of the introduced species impacts the biotic and abiotic components of the ecosystem.

3. As a class, discuss the following:

   a. Which of these introduced species, if any, should be controlled?

   b. For those species that should be controlled, what would be some effective ways of controlling them? Be sure to discuss the trade-offs of the different solutions.

ANALYSIS

1. How do you think the number of introduced species in the United States will change over the next 50 years? Explain your reasoning.

2. Imagine a friend of yours has a pet fish that they no longer want, and they plan to release it into the local stream. Write an email message to this friend about what might happen as a consequence of this action.

3. If you were going to become a scientist or engineer to help solve problems around invasive species, what kinds of skills and knowledge should you have?

Ecology

UNIT SUMMARY

Resource Availability

Ecology is the study of organisms and their interactions with other organisms and the physical environment. All of these interacting biotic and abiotic components make up an ecosystem. How well an organism does in its environment depends on its ability to acquire all of the resources it needs to grow, survive, and reproduce. One important resource is food, which provides an organism with the matter and energy it requires for these processes. When the availability of resources remains the same, a population of organisms may be stable over time. When resource availability changes, population size may change.

Population Ecology

Ecologists use many methods to determine population size. One such method is the transect method. By sampling the population in a systematic way, ecologists can estimate the size of a population in different environments and over time. This allows them to detect patterns and relationships between the organisms and other components in the ecosystem. For example, a population's increase in size may cause populations of other organisms to change in size also. Ecologists use models to describe relationships and to explain how an ecosystem functions. When the models focus on feeding relationships, they are called food *webs*. Ecologists use food webs to predict how changing one component within an ecosystem's feeding relationships may affect other components.

Cycling of Matter

All ecosystems have producers, like plants and algae, that use energy from the sun and matter in the form of water and carbon dioxide to make their own food. This process is known as *photosynthesis*. Producers can store this food or use it immediately. Consumers, organisms like animals, get their food by eating other organisms—consumers, producers, or both. Both producers and consumers break down food through cellular respiration to get the energy and matter they need for growth, survival, and reproduction. Decomposers are organisms that feed on dead and decaying organisms, breaking them down into carbon dioxide and water that can be used again by producers. In this way, matter cycles through ecosystems.

Flow of Energy

In contrast to matter, energy cannot be recycled in an ecosystem. At each level of the food web, only 10% of the energy in that level is available to the next level. The remaining 90% of the energy leaves the food web as heat. Eventually, because of the lessening energy available to the next level, additional levels cannot be supported. Thus, energy flows into, through, and out of a food web.

Interactions in Ecosystems

Biotic interactions follow predictable patterns across all ecosystems. Organisms that require the same resources to survive, grow, and reproduce are competitors for those resources. An animal that eats other animals is a predator, and one that is eaten by other animals is considered prey. Organisms can be harmed by other organisms through parasitism, or they can benefit from other organisms through mutualism. Understanding all of these interactions is essential to understanding how ecosystems function and how they may change over time.

Disruptions

Disruptions to ecosystems happen naturally due to small and large events. When a disruption is small and short term, ecosystems typically return to how they were before the disruption. When the disruption is large and happens over a long period of time, the ecosystem may change forever. Disruptions can be caused by natural disasters, such as fires, volcanoes, landslides, and extreme weather conditions. They can also be caused by human activity, including habitat destruction, over-hunting, or the introduction of a new species into an area where it has never occurred before. While most of the time these introductions do not affect the ecosystem, in some cases they have a very large impact because of the effects on the food web. When the introduced species is a plant, it may outcompete other plants for space. If it is an animal, it may outcompete other animals and cause the decline of these other species. When the introduced species is a predator, it may cause the decline of prey species that have no defenses against the new predator. Introduced species may also cause harm to humans through effects on health or the economy.

Design Solutions

Because of the harmful effects of introduced species for both ecosystems and humans, scientists and engineers are working to design solutions to these problems. Evaluating these possible solutions requires developing criteria and defining constraints. The optimal solution to problems caused by introduced species often depends on whether the problem affects natural ecosystems or human-built structures. Solutions to these problems require the input from people with knowledge in science, engineering, economics, and social science.

Key Science Terms

abiotic component	interaction
biotic component	matter
competitor	mutualism
constraint	parasitism
criteria	population
disruption	predator
ecology	prey
ecosystem	resource
energy	stability
food web	

A Science and Engineering

THE NATURE OF SCIENCE AND ENGINEERING

IF SOMEONE ASKED YOU the question, "What is science?" how would you answer?

You might reply that it is knowledge of such subjects as Biology, Chemistry, Earth Science, and Physics. That would be only partly correct. Although science is certainly related to the accumulation and advancement of knowledge, it is much more than that. Science is a way of exploring and understanding the natural world.

According to the American Association for the Advancement of Science (AAAS), two of the most fundamental aspects of science are that the world is understandable and that scientific ideas are subject to change.

Scientists believe that the world is understandable because things happen in consistent patterns that we can eventually understand through careful study. Observations must be made and data collected for us to discover the patterns that exist in the universe. At times scientists have to invent the instruments that allow them to collect this data. Eventually, they develop theories to explain the observations and patterns. The principles on which a theory is based apply throughout the universe.

When new knowledge becomes available, it is sometimes necessary to change theories. This most often means making small adjustments, but on rare occasions it means completely revising a theory. Although scientists can never be 100% certain about a theory, as knowledge about the universe becomes more sophisticated most theories become more refined and more widely accepted. You will see examples of this process as you study the history of scientists' understanding of such topics as elements and the periodic table, the cellular basis of life, genetics, plate tectonics, the solar system, and the universe in this middle school science program.

While the main goal of science is to understand phenomena, the main goal of engineering is to solve problems. Like science, engineering involves both knowledge and a set of practices common across a range of engineering problems. Just as scientists start by asking questions, engineers start by defining problems. Just as scientists search for explanations for phenomena, engineers search for solutions to problems.

Science and engineering often build on each other. For example, scientists use instruments developed by engineers to study the natural world. And engineers use scientific principles when designing solutions to problems.

Scientific Inquiry

Inquiry is at the heart of science, and an important component of inquiry is scientific investigation, including experimentation. Although scientists do not necessarily follow a series of fixed steps when conducting investigations, they share common understandings about the characteristics of a scientifically valid investigation. For example, scientists obtain evidence from observations and measurements. They repeat and confirm observations and ask other scientists to review their results. It is important for scientists to avoid bias in designing, conducting, and reporting their investigations and to have other unbiased scientists duplicate their results. Some types of investigations allow scientists to set up controls and vary just one condition at a time. They formulate and test hypotheses, sometimes collecting data that lead them to develop theories.

When scientists develop theories they are constructing models and explanations of the patterns and relationships they observe in natural phenomena. These explanations must be logically consistent with the evidence they have gathered and with evidence other scientists have gathered. Hypotheses and theories allow scientists to make predictions. If testing turns out to not support a prediction, scientists may have to look at revising the hypothesis or theory on which the prediction was based.

Engineering Design

An engineer uses science and technology to build a product or design a process that solves a problem or makes the world better. Engineering design refers to the process engineers use to design, test, and improve solutions to problems. Like scientists, engineers design investigations to test their ideas, use mathematics, analyze their data, and develop models.

Since most solutions in the real world are not perfect, engineers work to develop the best solutions they can, while balancing such factors as the function, cost, safety, and usability of their solutions. The factors engineers identify as important for solutions to a problem are called criteria and constraints. Most engineering solutions have one or more trade-offs—desired features that must be given up in order to gain other more desirable features.

Science as a Human Endeavor

Science and engineering are human activities. People from all over the world engage in science and engineering and use scientific information and technological solutions. The types of questions a scientist asks and the types of problems an engineer tries to solve are influenced by what they think is important. And what they think is important to investigate often depends on their background, experiences, and perspective. This is why it is essential for all types of people to become scientists and engineers—to be sure science and engineering respond to their interests and needs and to be sure that there are diverse ideas to enrich explanations and arguments. Participation by a wide variety of people in science and engineering will lead to greater and swifter progress toward understanding how the natural world works and solving problems facing individuals, communities, and the environment.

Visit the *SEPUP Third Edition* page for each unit of the SEPUP website at *www.sepuplhs.org/middle/third-edition* to learn more about the interests and accomplishments of diverse scientists and engineers. Each unit highlights examples of people from varied backgrounds in careers that contribute to and depend on the advancement of science and technology.

References

American Association for the Advancement of Science (AAAS). (1990). Project 2061: Science for all Americans. New York: Oxford University Press.

National Research Council. (2012). *A Framework for K–12 Science Education: Practices, Crosscutting Concepts, and Core Ideas.* Committee on a Conceptual Framework for New K–12 Science Education Standards. Board on Science Education, Division of Behavioral and Social Sciences and Education. Washington, DC: The National Academies Press.

B Science Safety

SCIENCE SAFETY GUIDELINES

YOU ARE RESPONSIBLE FOR your own safety and for the safety of others. Be sure you understand the following guidelines and follow your teacher's instructions for all laboratory and field activities.

Before the Investigation

- Listen carefully to your teacher's instructions, and follow any steps recommended when preparing for the activity.

- Know the location and proper use of emergency safety equipment, such as the safety eye-and-face wash, fire blanket, and fire extinguisher.

- Know the location of exits and the procedures for an emergency.

- Dress appropriately for lab work. Tie back long hair and avoid wearing dangling or bulky jewelry or clothing. Do not wear open-toed shoes. Avoid wearing synthetic fingernails—they are a fire hazard and can tear protective gloves.

- Tell your teacher if you wear contact lenses, have allergies to latex, food, or other items, or have any medical condition that may affect your ability to perform the lab safely.

- Make sure the worksurface and floor in your work area are clear of books, backpacks, purses, or other unnecessary materials.

- Ask questions if you do not understand the procedure or safety recommendations for an activity.

- Review, understand, and sign the Safety Agreement, and obtain the signature of a parent or guardian.

During the Investigation

- Carefully read and follow the activity procedure and safety recommendations.

- Follow any additional written and spoken instructions provided by your teacher.

- Use only those activities and materials approved by your teacher and needed for the investigation.

- Don't eat, drink, chew gum, or apply cosmetics in the lab area.

- Wear personal protective equipment (chemical splash goggles, lab aprons, and protective gloves) appropriate for the activity.

- Do not wear contact lenses when using chemicals. If your doctor says you must wear them, notify your teacher before conducting any activity that uses chemicals.

- Read all labels on chemicals, and be sure you are using the correct chemical.

- Keep chemical containers closed when not in use.

- Do not touch, taste, or smell any chemical unless you are instructed to do so by your teacher.

- Mix chemicals only as directed.

- Use caution when working with hot plates, hot liquids, electrical equipment, and glassware.

- Follow all directions when working with live organisms or microbial cultures.

- Be mature and cautious, and don't engage in horseplay.

- Report any unsafe situations, accidents, or chemical spills to your teacher immediately.

- If you spill chemicals on your skin, wash it for 15 minutes with large amounts of water. Remove any contaminated clothing and continue to rinse. Ask your teacher if you should take other steps, including seeking medical attention.

- Respect and take care of all equipment.

After the Investigation

- Dispose of all chemical and biological materials as instructed by your teacher.

- Clean up your work area, replace bottle caps securely, and follow any special instructions.

- Return equipment to its proper location.

- Wash your hands with soap and warm water for at least 20 seconds after any laboratory activity, even if you wore protective gloves.

Your teacher will give you an agreement similar to the one below to sign.

Science Safety Agreements

STUDENT

I, _____, have read the attached Science Safety Guidelines for students and have discussed them in my classroom. I understand my responsibilities for maintaining safety in the science classroom. I agree to follow these guidelines and any additional rules provided by the school district or my teacher.

Student Signature_____

Date_____

PARENT OR GUARDIAN

Please review with your student the attached Science Safety Guidelines, which include the safety responsibilities and expectations for all students. It is important that all students follow these guidelines in order to protect themselves, their classmates, and their teachers from accidents. Please contact the school if you have any questions about these guidelines.

I, _____, have read the attached guidelines and discussed them with my child. I understand that my student is responsible for following these guidelines and any additional instructions at all times.

Parent or Guardian Signature_____

Date_____

C Science Skills

N THE FOLLOWING PAGES are instructions you can use to review the following important science skills:

- Reading a Graduated Cylinder

- Using a Dropper Bottle

- Bar Graphing Checklist

- Scatterplot and Line Graphing Checklist

- Interpreting Graphs

- Elements of Good Experimental Design

- Using Microscopes

READING A GRADUATED CYLINDER

A graduated cylinder measures the volume of a liquid, usually in milliliters (mL). To measure correctly with a graduated cylinder:

1. Determine what measurement each unmarked line on the graduated cylinder represents.

2. Set the graduated cylinder on a flat surface and pour in the liquid to be measured.

3. Bring your eyes to the level of the fluid's surface. (You will need to bend down!)

4. Read the graduated cylinder at the lowest point of the liquid's curve (called the meniscus).

5. If the curve falls between marks, estimate the volume to the closest mL.

The example below shows a plastic graduated cylinder that contains 42 mL of liquid.

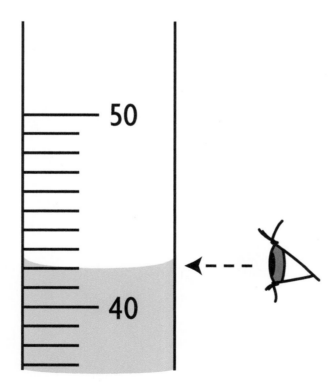

USING A DROPPER BOTTLE

Incorrect

Holding the dropper bottle at an angle gives drops that vary in size.

Correct

Holding the dropper bottle vertically gives drops that are more consistent in size.

BAR GRAPHING CHECKLIST

Sample Graph

Follow the instructions below to make a sample bar graph.

☐ Start with a table of data. This table represents the amount of Chemical A that the Acme Company used each year from 2011 to 2015.

Year	Chemical A used (kg)
2011	100
2012	80
2013	110
2014	90
2015	105

☐ Determine whether a bar graph is the best way to represent the data.

☐ If so, draw the axes. Label them with the names and units of the data.

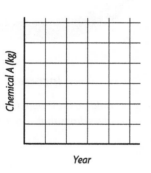

☐ Decide on a scale for each axis. Be sure there is enough space for all the data, but that it's not too crowded.

Year axis: 1 block = 1 year
Chemical A axis: 1 block = 20 kilograms

☐ Mark intervals on the graph, and label them clearly.

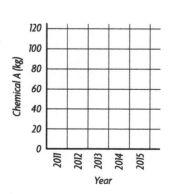

BAR GRAPHING CHECKLIST (continued)

☐ Plot your data on the graph.

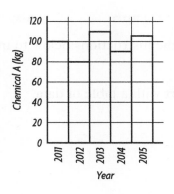

☐ Fill in the bars.

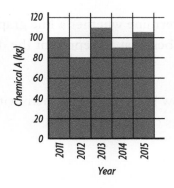

☐ Title your graph. The title should describe what the graph shows.

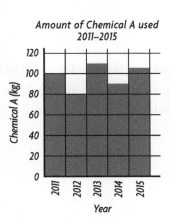

SCATTERPLOT AND LINE GRAPHING CHECKLIST

Sample Graph

Follow the instructions below to make a sample line graph.

☐ Start with a table of data.

MOTION OF A BALL

Time (minutes)	Distance (meters)
0	0
1	5
2	9
3	16
4	20
5	27

☐ Determine whether a line graph or a scatterplot is the best way to represent the data.

LINE GRAPH

☐ Draw the axes. Label them with the names and units of the data.

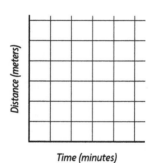

☐ Decide on a scale for each axis. Be sure there is enough space for all the data, but that it's not too crowded.

Time axis: 1 block = 1 minute
Distance axis: 1 block = 5 meters

☐ Draw intervals on the graph, and label them clearly.

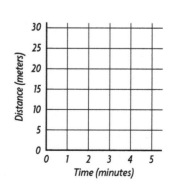

SCATTERPLOT AND LINE GRAPHING CHECKLIST (continued)

☐ Plot your data on the graph.

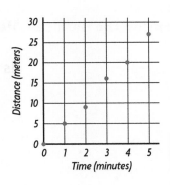

☐ For a scatterplot, leave the points unconnected.

For a line graph, draw a smooth line or curve that follows the pattern indicated by the position of the points.

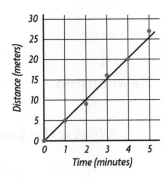

☐ Title your graph. The title should describe what the graph shows.

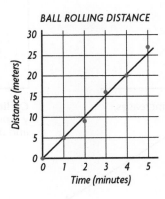

☐ If more than one data set has been plotted, include a key

● = *large ball*
○ = *small ball*

INTERPRETING GRAPHS

Determine the path that describes the data

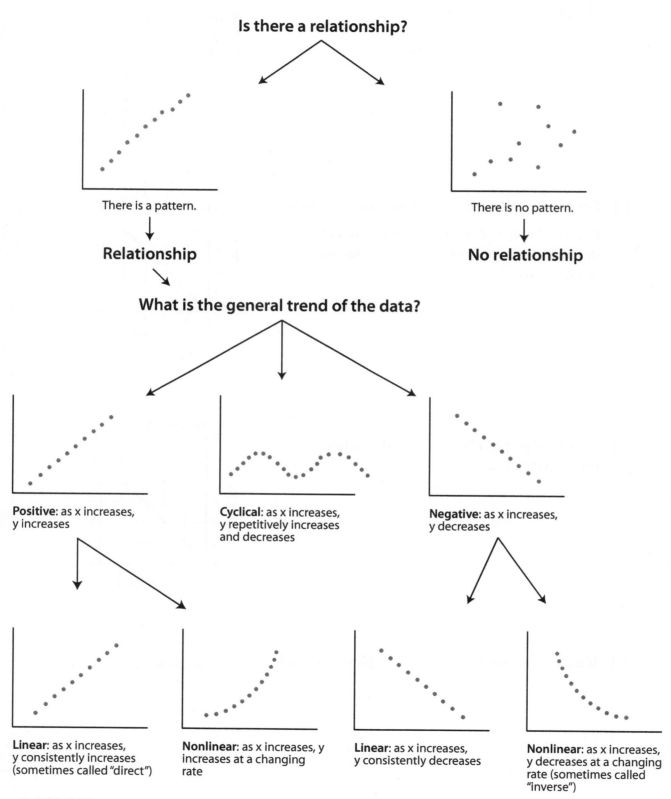

Is there a relationship?

There is a pattern.

There is no pattern.

Relationship

No relationship

What is the general trend of the data?

Positive: as x increases, y increases

Cyclical: as x increases, y repetitively increases and decreases

Negative: as x increases, y decreases

Linear: as x increases, y consistently increases (sometimes called "direct")

Nonlinear: as x increases, y increases at a changing rate

Linear: as x increases, y consistently decreases

Nonlinear: as x increases, y decreases at a changing rate (sometimes called "inverse")

INTERPRETING GRAPHS (continued)

Define the components of the graph.

Things you can say:

"The title of the graph is…"

"The independent variable in this graph is…"

"The dependent variable in this graph is…"

"_____ is measured in _____"

Create a description of what the graph reveals.

Things you can say:

"This graph shows…"

"As the _____ increases, the…"

"The _____ has the highest…"

"_____ is different from _____ because…"

"The_____ peaked at…"

"The rate of _____ increased from…"

Describe how the graph relates to the topic.

Things you can say…

"This graph is important to understanding _____because…"

"This graph supports the claim that _____ because…."

"This graph refutes the claim that _____ because…."

ELEMENTS OF GOOD EXPERIMENTAL DESIGN

An experiment that is well designed:

- builds on previous research.

- is based on a question, observation, or hypothesis.

- describes all steps in a procedure clearly and completely.

- includes a control for comparison.

- keeps all variables—except the one being tested—the same.

- describes all data to be collected.

- includes precise measurements and all records of data collected during experiment.

- may require multiple trials.

- can be reproduced by other investigators.

- respects human and animal subjects.

Note: Elements may vary, depending on the problem being studied.

USING MICROSCOPES

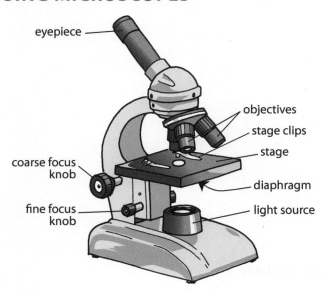

eyepiece

objectives

stage clips

stage

coarse focus knob

diaphragm

fine focus knob

light source

Focusing a Microscope

Be sure that your microscope is set on the lowest power before placing your slide onto the microscope stage. Place the slide on the microscope stage. Center the slide so that the sample is directly over the light opening, and adjust the microscope settings as necessary. If the microscope has stage clips, secure the slide in position so that it does not move.

- Observe the sample. Focus first with the coarse-focus knob, and then adjust the fine-focus knob.

- After switching to a higher power magnification, be careful to adjust the focus with the fine-focus knob only.

- Return to low power before removing the slide from the microscope stage.

Safety

Always carry a microscope properly with both hands—one hand underneath and one holding the microscope arm. When you are working with live organisms, be sure to wash your hands thoroughly after you finish the laboratory.

Spirogyra (algae) x 400

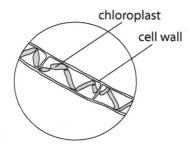

chloroplast

cell wall

Some Tips for Better Drawings:

- Use a sharp pencil and have a good eraser available.

- Try to relax your eyes when looking through the eyepiece. You can cover one eye or learn to look with both eyes open. Try not to squint.

- Look through your microscope at the same time as you do your drawing. Look through the microscope more than you look at your paper.

- Don't draw every small thing on your slide. Just concentrate on one or two of the most common or interesting things.

- You can draw things larger than you actually see them. This helps you show all of the details you see.

- Keep written words outside the circle.

- Use a ruler to draw the lines for your labels. Keep lines parallel— do not cross one line over another.

- Remember to record the level of magnification next to your drawing.

APPENDIX

D The International System of Units

MEASUREMENTS THAT APPEAR IN this program are expressed in metric units from the International System of Units, otherwise known as SI units (from Système Internationale d'Unités), which was established by international agreement. Virtually all countries in the world mandate use of the metric system exclusively. The United States does not use the metric system for many measurements, although it has been the standard for the scientific community in the United States for more than 200 years. A U.S. government effort to convert from the United States customary system to metric measurements in all realms of life has yet to extend far beyond governmental agencies, the military, and some industries.

The reason that many countries have replaced their traditional measurement systems with the metric system is its ease of use and to improve international trade. There are far fewer units to understand in comparison to the system commonly used in the United States. The metric system has only one base unit for each quantity and larger or smaller units are expressed by adding a prefix. The table below shows the base units in the International System of Units.

Quantity	Base unit
Length	meter (m)
Mass	kilogram (kg)
Time	second (s)
Temperature	kelvin (K)
Electric current	ampere (A)
Luminous intensity	candela (cd)
Mole	mole (mol)

Other international units appearing in SEPUP's Issues and Science units are shown in the table below.

Quantity	Unit	Common example
Temperature	Celsius (°C)	Room temperature is about 20° Celsius.
Volume	liter (L)	A large soda bottle contains 2 liters.
Mass	gram (g)	A dollar bill has the mass of about 1 gram.
Wavelength	nanometer (nm)	Visible light is in the range of 400 to 780 nanometers.

The International System's prefixes change the magnitude of the units by factors of 1,000. Prefixes indicate which multiple of a thousand is applied. For example, the prefix kilo- means 1,000. Therefore, a kilometer is 1,000 meters and a kilogram is 1,000 grams. To convert a quantity from one unit to another in the metric system, the quantity needs only to be multiplied or divided by multiples of 1,000. The chart below shows the prefixes for the metric system in relation to the base units. Note: Although it is not a multiple of 1,000 the prefix *centi-* is commonly used, for example, in the unit centimeter. Centi- represents a factor of one 100th.

Metric prefix	Factor	Factor (numerical)
giga (G)	one billion	1,000,000,000
mega (M)	one million	1,000,000
kilo (k)	one thousand	1,000
<UNIT>	one	1
milli (m)	one one-thousandth	1/1,000
micro (μ)	one one-millionth	1/1,000,000
nano (n)	one one-billionth	1/1,000,000,000

APPENDIX

Literacy Strategies

IN THE FOLLOWING PAGES are templates or instructions for some of the literacy strategies that are used throughout this book. Use them for reference or to copy into your science notebook.

- Oral Presentations

- Reading Scientific Procedures

- Keeping a Science Notebook

- Writing a Formal Investigation Report

- Instructions for Constructing a Concept Map

- Developing Communication Skills

ORAL PRESENTATIONS

- Your presentation time is short. Focus your presentation on the most important ideas you need to communicate.

- Communicate clearly by planning your words in advance. When speaking, talk slowly and loudly, and look at your audience.

- Group members should ask for and give each other support if they need help expressing a key word or concept.

- Include graphs and maps when possible. Make sure the type or handwriting and the images are large enough for everyone in the audience to see them.

- While you have your own opinions on a topic, it is important that you present unbiased and complete information. Your audience can then make their own conclusions.

- All the members of a group must participate.

- Since any group member may be asked to answer questions from the class, all group members should fully understand the presentation.

- In a group presentation, you could all play the role of different experts when presenting your information. The class would represent the community members who might be making a decision on the issue.

READING SCIENTIFIC PROCEDURES

The purpose of reading a scientific procedure is to find out exactly what to do, when to do it and with what materials, in order to complete all the steps of an investigation.

If you read a step and are not sure what to do, try these strategies:

- Re-read the previous step.

- Re-read the step that confuses you. Sometimes re-reading clarifies the information.

- Ask your partner if he or she understands what the step says to do.

- Ask your partner if there are words you don't understand.

- Ask your partner to explain what the step says to do.

- Ask your partner to read the step aloud as you listen and try to do what your partner is describing.

- Re-read the purpose (Challenge) of the investigation.

- Try to say the purpose of the step out loud in your own words.

- Look at the clues in the pictures of the activity.

- Peek at other groups and listen to see if they are doing the step that confuses you.

- Tell your teacher exactly what you are confused about and why it doesn't make sense.

KEEPING A SCIENCE NOTEBOOK

- Write in blue or black ink.

- Cross out mistakes or changes with a single line. Do not erase or use correction fluid.

- Write neatly.

- Record the date of each entry.

- For each new investigation, write down your:

  Title:

  Purpose:
  Re-write the Challenge question in your own words.
  Hint: What are you going to do? Why are you going to do it?

  Materials:
  Place a "√" here after you have collected the necessary materials.

  Procedure:
  Write down whether you understand the procedure.

  Data:
  Record observations, measurements, and other lab work.
  Include data tables, charts, diagrams, and/or graphs when needed.
  Be sure to label your work clearly.

- Sometimes, you may want to:

  Make inferences or draw conclusions based on the data.
  I think my results mean …
  I think that this happened because …

  Reflect on how the activity worked in your group.
  This is what went well . . This is what did not go well …
  If I could do this activity again, I would …

  Think about what questions you still have.
  I wonder if …
  I'm not sure about …

  Keep track of new vocabulary and ideas.
  A key word I learned is …
  I would like to find out what happens when …
  One interesting thing to do would be to …

KEEPING A SCIENCE NOTEBOOK (continued)

The following is a guide to help you conduct investigations. However, depending on the investigation, you may not always use all of steps below or use them in the same order each time.

Title: Choose a title that describes the investigation.

Purpose: What am I looking for? Write what you are trying to find out in the form of a question.

Background: What do I know about the topic? Write a summary of background information you have on the topic that led to the purpose for the investigation.

Hypothesis: Write a statement about what you predict you will see as data in the experiment to answer the question in the "Purpose" and why you are making that prediction.

Experimental Design: How will you answer the question?

Describe the methods you will use (what you will do) to answer the question.

Use short numbered steps that are easy to follow in the lab.

Make a list of the materials you will use to answer the question.

Outline the variables:

- Independent variable (what is being changed)
- Dependent variable (what is being measured)
- Control (what will be used as baseline comparison

Data: What did you find?

Record observations and measurements.

Use a data table where appropriate to organize the data.

Don't forget to include proper units and clear labels.

At the end of your investigation:

Make inferences or draw conclusions about the data:

I think my results mean …

I think this happened because …

Think about any errors that occurred during the investigation:

What did not go as planned?

What steps were hard to follow while doing the investigation and why?

Think about questions you still have that could lead to new investigations:

I wonder if …

I'm not sure about …

Keep track of new vocabulary and new ideas that could lead to new investigations

I would like to find out what happens when …

One interesting thing to do would be to …

Reflect on how the activity worked in your group

This is what went well …This is what did not go well …

If I could do this investigation again, I would …

WRITING A FORMAL INVESTIGATION REPORT (continued)

Use the information from your science notebook to write a formal report on the investigation you performed.

Title:

Choose a title that describes the investigation.

Abstract: What were you looking for in this investigation, and what did you find?

Write a paragraph that summarizes what you already knew about the topic, your purpose, your hypothesis, and your results and conclusions.

Experimental Design:

Describe the materials and investigational methods you used to answer the question.

State what variables you worked with and any controls.

Data: What did you find?

Report observations and measurements. Include an organized data table if appropriate to help someone reviewing your report to easily see the results.

Don't forget to use proper units of measurement and write clear labels for your table columns.

Data Analysis: Represent the data in a way that can be easily interpreted.

Use graphs, diagrams, or charts where appropriate to help a reviewer interpret your data.

Conclusion: What do the data mean?

Summarize the data.

Discuss your conclusion based on the accuracy of your hypothesis and the data you collected.

Discuss any errors that occurred that may have interfered with the results.

Describe any changes that need to be made the next time the investigation is performed.

Describe any new questions to be investigated based on the results of this investigation.

INSTRUCTIONS FOR CONSTRUCTING A CONCEPT MAP

1. Work with your group to create a list of 15–20 words related to the topic.

2. If you are uncertain of the meaning of a word, look it up in the book or your notes or discuss it with your group.

3. Discuss with your group how all of the words on your list are related, and sort your list of words into 3–5 categories based on these relationships.

   Remember to listen to and consider the ideas of other members of your group. If you disagree with others in your group, explain to the rest of the group why you disagree.

4. Identify words that can be used to describe each category.

5. Work with your group to create a concept map on this topic. Follow these steps:

   a. Write the topic in the center of your paper, and circle it.

   b. Place the words describing each category around the topic. Circle each word.

   c. Draw a line between the topic and each category. On each line, explain the relationship between the topic and the category.

   d. Repeat Steps 5b and 5c as you continue to add all of the words on your list to your concept map.

   e. Add lines to connect other related words. Explain the relationship between the words on the line.

6. View the concept maps of other groups. As you look at their concept maps, observe similarities and differences between their maps and yours. Discuss your observations with your group members.

Name _____ Date _____

DEVELOPING COMMUNICATION SKILLS

COMMUNICATION	SENTENCE STARTERS
To better understand	One point that was not clear to me was . . . Are you saying that . . . Can you please clarify . . .
To share an idea	Another idea is to . . . What if we tried . . . I have an idea. We could try . . .
To disagree	I see your point, but what about . . . Another way of looking at it is . . . I'm still not convinced that . . .
To challenge	How did you reach the conclusion that . . . What makes you think that . . . How does it explain . . .
To look for feedback	What would help me improve . . . Does it make sense, what I said about . . .
To provide positive feedback	One strength of your idea is . . . Your idea is good because . . . I have an idea. We coud try . . .
To provide constructive feedback	The argument would be stronger if . . . Another way to do it would be . . . What if you said it like this . . .
To discuss information presented in text and graphics	I'm not sure I completely understand this, but I think it may mean... I know something about this from... A question I have about this is... If we look at the graphic, it shows...

F *Media Literacy*

MAGINE YOURSELF READING A magazine. A feature article summarizes recent studies on the effectiveness of vitamin supplements and concludes that taking vitamin pills and liquids is a waste of money. A few pages later, an advertisement from a vitamin company claims that one of its products will protect you from all sorts of diseases. Such wide differences in claims that you will see in the popular media are common, but how can you tell which one is correct? "Media literacy" is the term that encompasses the skills we need to develop to effectively analyze and evaluate the barrage of information we encounter every day. Media literacy also includes the ability to use various media to create and communicate our own messages.

A strong background in the process of science helps you build two important skills of media literacy: being able to identify valid and adequate evidence behind a claim and evaluating if the claim is a logical conclusion based on the evidence. The skills share much in common with the process of scientific inquiry, in which you learn to seek out information, assess the information, and come to a conclusion based on your findings.

Evaluating Media Messages

A "media message" is an electronic, digital, print, audible, or artistic visual message created to transmit information. Media messages can include newspaper articles, political advertisements, speeches, artwork, or even billboards. The following are some of the kinds of questions you might ask as you learn to critically analyze and evaluate messages from various kinds of media. On the next page are three examples of media messages, all related to a common theme. Use these three examples to analyze and evaluate the messages.

BAY MEDICAL JOURNAL
The Monthly Journal of the Bay Region Medical Society
Vol. XXXIV, No. 8

Vitamin Z reduces severity of the common cold by 15%

P. M. Chakravarty, M.D., Harbord University Medical School, Clinical Studies Department
Loretta Arrienza, Ph.D., University of the Bay Region, Department of Epidemiology
Mary S. Lowe, M.D., Mid-Bay Hospital, Director of Patient Care
William Ness, M.P.H., N.P., Mid-Bay Hospital, Director of Nursing

ABSTRACT: IN A TWELVE-MONTH STUDY with 626 healthy male and female participants aged 21–36 and located in the general Bay region, the authors found that a reg____ ___e of Vitamin Z appeared to reduce the severity of the common cold by 15%. In this controlled ___ __ received a placebo, and ___ dose did not 313 participants received a 500 mg dose _f _i_amin Z ___ ___ in th___ know which ___ ___ ___ ___ach, ___ __rt ___

BEFORE   AFTER

OUR DOCTOR-APPROVED
VITAMINS PUT YOU BACK
ON YOUR FEET! Try
HEALTH-GLOWW TODA___
Super savings:
600 for the price of 50___
Call now! **1-999-997-___**

HOME & HEALTH Magazine

September

Are VITAMINS a WASTE of your money?

SUZANNE BERYL WALKER

Donna S. was wondering if vitamins might give her the energy and good health that she felt had been slipping away ever since she had moved to Springfield with her family for a new job.

1. Who created this message?

Is this person an expert in the content of the message? What credentials does this person have that would make them an expert in this topic? Does this person have any conflicts of interest that may make him or her biased in any way? Who sponsored (or paid for) the message? Does the source of funding have any conflicts of interest?

2. **What creative techniques in the message attract a person's attention?**

   Are there any sensational or emotional words, images, or sounds that grab the viewer's attention? Do any of these words, images, or sounds try to stir up emotions and influence the viewer's ideas?

3. **Does the message cite or mention appropriate sources of factual information?**

   Does the author cite first-person sources when reporting facts? Are the author's sources from credible organizations?

4. **Does the presented evidence completely support the claim?**

   Might there be other information that could support or discredit the message? Does the author make logical inferences and conclusions from the evidence presented in the article?

5. **Who is the target audience of this message?**

   How is this message directed at this particular audience?

6. **Is the message promoting certain values, lifestyles, positions, or ideas either directly or indirectly?**

   Are there any positions or ideas that are being promoted that are not explicit in the message?

Evaluating Internet Sources

Imagine that you want to search the Internet to find out about the effectiveness of vitamin supplements so that you can come to your own conclusion. When you are searching for information online, a search engine is searching from over one trillion websites.[1] Determining which websites and sources of information are reliable and which are biased is difficult. To make an informed decision about this topic, you will need to identify accurate and unbiased websites. Below is a suggested list of questions that will help you determine if a particular website is an accurate and unbiased source of information.

1. **Are the authors' names, contact information, and credentials clearly labeled on the website?**

   Accurate websites will usually contain information from knowledgeable authors who have their names, credentials, and contact information clearly labeled on the website. Some websites are managed by a collection of people or an organization, and information on the exact author may not be clearly stated. However,

1. Alpert, Jesse & Hajaj, Nissan. (July 25, 2008). We knew the Web was big. . . . *The Official Google Blog. Retrieved August 2010 from* http://googleblog.blogspot.com/ 2008/07/we-knew-web-was-big.html.

these organizations should state the names, contact information, and credentials somewhere on their website of the people who represent the organization.

2. **Is the information and the website up to date?**

Some information that you may be seeking needs to be current. For example, if you were looking for the number of cars in the United States, you would want the most recent data. A study conducted in 1982 would not be helpful in this case. When seeking information that needs to be current, determine if the date the article or information was written is clearly indicated on the website so you can be sure you are accessing the most recent information. Credible websites will usually indicate the date the article or information was created or last updated. Also, the person or organization maintaining the website should be regularly updating the website, so that the majority of links to other websites work.

3. **Are sources of information clearly cited?**

When factual information is stated in a website, is the source clearly cited so you can refer back to it?

4. **Are there links to more resources on this topic?**

Authoritative websites will often provide links to further information from other sources that support their claim. Authors of websites that contain information that is biased or inaccurate usually do not provide additional information that supports their claims.

5. **What are other people saying about the author or the organization that produced this information?**

If you come across information from an author or organization that you are unfamiliar with, perform a search for other information about the author or organization. What are experts writing about the author's or organization's other work?

6. **Why is this website on the Internet?**

Was this information put on the Internet to inform or to persuade people? Is the author selling something? What is the author's motivation for providing this information?

Further Resources

Marlene Thier & Bennett Daviss. (2002). *The New Science Literacy*. Heinemann: Portsmouth, NH.

Center for Media Literacy. http://www.medialit.org.

PBS Teachers. Media literacy. http://www.pbs.org/teachers/media_lit.

G *Crosscutting Concepts*

PATTERNS	A pattern is a set of repeating things or events. Scientists observe patterns in their data. Patterns lead to questions about relationships and ideas about what causes these relationships.
CAUSE AND EFFECT **A → B**	Events have causes. If "A" causes "B" to happen, they have a cause-and-effect relationship. A major activity of science is to explain how this happens. Sometimes the causes are simple and sometimes they are complex. Sometimes both A and B occur, but one does not cause the other.
SCALE, PROPORTION, AND QUANTITY	Scientific phenomena occur at various scales of size, time, and energy. Phenomena observed at one scale may not be observable at another scale. Scientists use proportional relationships to compare measurements of objects and events. They often use mathematical expressions and equations to represent these relationships.
SYSTEM AND SYSTEM MODELS	A system is a group of interacting objects or processes. Describing a system, including its components, interactions and boundaries, and making models of that system helps scientists and engineers understand phenomena and test ideas.
ENERGY AND MATTER	Tracking changes of energy and matter into, out of, and within systems helps scientists understand the systems' possibilities and limitations. Many cause and effect relationships result from changes of energy and matter.
STRUCTURE AND FUNCTION	The structure (shape, composition, construction) of an object or living thing determines many of its properties and functions (what the structure can do).
STABILITY AND CHANGE	For natural and built systems alike, conditions are sometimes stable (the same or within a range), and sometimes they change. Scientists study what conditions lead to either stability or change.

Glossary

abiotic The nonliving components in an ecosystem include water, temperature, and sunlight.

advantage A property that, in your opinion, is favorable.

biodiversity The variety of life at every level, from genes to species to ecosystems.

biotic The living components in an ecosystem are the organisms.

cell The smallest structural unit, enclosed by a membrane, that makes up all living organisms.

cellular respiration A series of chemical reactions in a cell that break down sugars and release energy.

commensalism The relationship between two species where one species benefits while the other species is neither harmed nor helped.

competition The situation when two organisms or two species compete for the same resource.

constraint In engineering design, something that limits the solution to a problem.

consumer An organism that gets its food by eating other organisms.

correlation A relationship between one event or action and another. There may or may not be a causal relationship between two correlated events.

criteria In engineering design, the goals and the desired features of the solution.

data Information gathered from an experiment or observations.

decomposer An organism that gets its food from dead organisms and wastes from living organisms.

dependent variable The observed phenomenon that is being measured.

disadvantage A property that, in your opinion, is not favorable.

ecologist Scientists who study ecology.

ecology The study of the relationships of organisms to one another and to the physical environment.

ecosystem All of the living and nonliving components, and all of the interactions among them.

energy The ability to cause objects to change, move, or work.

energy transfer The transfer of energy from one object to another.

energy transformation The change of energy from one type to another, such as from chemical to heat.

error Variations between a measurement and the true value of a quantity.

evidence Information that supports or refutes a claim.

food web A diagram that models feeding relationships within an ecosystem.

habitat A location in an environment where an organism lives.

hypothesis A tentative theory used to explain a set of facts. A hypothesis can lead to further investigation to test whether the hypothesis is valid.

independent variable The controlled variable in an experiment.

infer To conclude by reasoning from known facts.

inference A conclusion based on observations or what is already known.

interpret To explain or give an account of facts with regard to the explainer's conception of what the facts mean.

introduced species Species that exist outside of the species' normal range because of human activity.

invasive species Introduced species that cause or have the ability to cause harm to the environment or people.

mass The amount of matter in an object.

matter The stuff that makes up all living and nonliving objects.

meter The fundamental unit of length in the metric (SI) system; 1 meter is equal to 100 centimeters.

model Any representation of a system or its components used to help one understand and communicate how it works.

mutualism The relationship between two species where both species benefit.

parasitism The relationship between two species where one species benefits while the other is harmed.

pattern Something that happens in a repeated and predictable way.

photosynthesis The process by which plants convert water and carbon dioxide into sugars and oxygen.

population A group of organisms of the same species living in the same habitat.

predator An organism that eats another living organism.

prey An organism that is eaten by another organism.

producer An organism that produces its own food.

quadrat A square or rectangular plot of land marked off, to determine where to collect their samples.

range In ecology, the total of all the areas where a species lives.

rate A ratio of two different kinds of measurement.

scientific model, See *model*.

species A group of individuals that actually or potentially interbreed in nature.

stable Not changing or resistant to change.

structure The parts of an object or system, including what they are made of, their shapes, and their arrangement

symbiosis The close and often long-term interaction between two species.

technology The application of science to make practical things for everyday life and for use especially in industrial manufacturing and for commercial purposes.

temperature A measure of the amount of molecular motion, generally using the Fahrenheit (°F) or Celsius (°C) scale.

tested variable A variable that is changed in a systematic way in an experiment or investigation in order to determine its effect.

trade-off A desirable outcome given up to gain another desirable outcome.

transect The specific path or area, often marked with a rope or measuring tape showing where data should be collected.

variable A changing factor. In an experiment, the variable is what is studied, such as the effect of amplitude of a wave on the energy it transmits.

Index

Bold page number indicates a definition. *Italic* page number indicates an illustration.

Credits

Abbreviations: t (top), m (middle), b (bottom), l (left), r (right), c (center)

All illustrations by Seventeenth Street Studios

Front cover photo and unit opener (Purple Loosestrife): ©Jeff Lepore/ Science Source

Page 4: Faintsmoke; Page 5: ©Frank Lane Picture Agency/CORBIS; Page 9: ©S. van Mechelen, courtesy of the Exotic Species Graphics Library; Page 11: t: ©Buddy Mays/CORBIS, b: courtesy of Jack Leonard, New Orleans Mosquito Control Board; Page 12: t: National Park Service; Page 12: b: ©O. Alamany & E. Vicens/CORBIS; Page 13: t: Jason Lindsey/Alamy Stock Photo, b: Martha L. Walter, Michigan Sea Grant;; Page 14: t: ©Lynda Richardson/CORBIS, b: Public Domain; Page 15: Tom Koerner/USFWS, Page 16: tl: Monterey Bay Sanctuary: Oceanography Monitoring Project, bl: NOAA, r: National Park Service; Page 17: l: Justin Meissen r: Justin Meissen; Page 24: l: Visa Vietnam, r: E. A. Janes/Science Source; Page 27: ©Gary Kramer/ National Resources Conservation Service; Page 29: l: Katherine Johnson, r: Ted Kinsman/Science Source; Page 35: Orin Zebest; Page 39: Ralph Daily; Page 40: Ketzirah Lesser & Art Drauglis; Page 41: Frauke Feind; Page: 44 PDPics; Page 47: Nguyen Tan Tin/ Nikon Small World; Page 48: Vince Smith; Page 55: ©AFP/CORBIS; Page 57: GLSGN Exotic Species Library; Page 60: Ken Marshall; Page 67: Stephen Stewart, Michigan Sea Grant; Page 69: Peter Yates/ The LIFE Images Collection/Getty Images.

Kids' Travel Guide
Germany

FlyingKids® Presents:
Kids' Travel Guide
Germany

Author: Salomé G.

Editor: Carma Graber

Graphic designer: Neboysha Dolovacki

Cover Illustrations and design: Francesca Guido

Published by FlyingKids® Limited

Visit us @ www.theflyingkids.com

Contact us: leonardo@theflyingkids.com

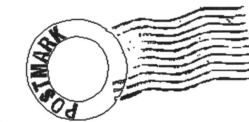

ISBN: 978-1-910994-13-9

Acknowledgment:

All images are from Shutterstock or public domain except those mentioned below:

Depositphotos: 9mt, 28t, 30mc, 30mb, 35bg.

Key: t=top; b=bottom; l=left; r=right; c=center; m=main image; bg=background

Table of Contents

This is the only page for parents in this book ...

Dear Parents,

If you bought this book, you're probably planning a family trip with your kids. You are spending a lot of time and money in the hopes that this family vacation will be pleasant and fun. You would like your children to learn a little about the country you visit — its geography, history, unique culture, traditions, and more. And you hope they will always remember the trip as a very special experience.

The reality is often quite different. Parents find themselves frustrated as they struggle to convince their kids to join a tour or visit a landmark, while the kids just want to stay in and watch TV. On the road, the children are glued to their mobile devices instead of enjoying the new sights and scenery — or they complain and constantly ask, "When are we going to get there?" Many parents are disappointed after they return home and discover that their kids don't remember much about the trip and the new things they learned.

That's exactly why *Kids' Travel Guide — Germany* was created.

How does it work?

A family trip is fun. But difficulties can arise when children are not in their natural environment. *Kids' Travel Guide — Germany* takes this into account and supports children as they get ready for the trip, visit new places, learn new things, and finally, return home.

Kids' Travel Guide — Germany does this by helping children to prepare for the trip and know what to expect. During the trip, kids will read relevant facts about Germany and get advice on how to adapt to new situations. The kids will meet Leonardo — their tour guide. Leonardo encourages them to experiment, explore, and be more involved in the family's activities — as well as to learn new information and make memories throughout the trip.

Kids' Travel Guide — Germany includes puzzles, tasks to complete, useful tips, and other recommendations along the way. In addition, kids are asked to document and write about their experiences during the trip, so that when you return home, they will have a memoir that will be fun to look at and reread again and again.

Kids' Travel Guide — Germany offers general information about Germany, so it is useful regardless of the city or part of the country you plan to visit. It includes basic geography; flag, symbols, and coins; basic history; and colorful facts about culture and customs in Germany.

Ready for a new experience?
Have a nice trip and have fun!

Hi, Kids!

If you are reading this book, it means you are lucky—you are going to **Germany**!

You probably already know what areas you will visit, and you may have noticed that **your parents** are getting ready for the journey. They have bought **travel guides**, looked for information on the **Internet**, and **printed pages** of information. They are talking to friends and people who have already visited **Germany**, in order to learn about it and know what to do, where to go, and when … But this is not just another **guidebook** for your parents.

THIS BOOK IS FOR YOU ONLY—THE YOUNG TRAVELER.

So what is this book all about?

First and foremost, meet **Leonardo**, your very own personal guide on this trip. **Leonardo** has visited many places around the **world** (guess how he got there 😜), and he will be with you throughout the **book** and the **trip**. **Leonardo** will tell you all **about** the **places** you will visit—it is always good to learn a little bit about the country and its history beforehand. He will provide many **ideas**, **quizzes**, **tips**, and **other surprises**. **Leonardo** will accompany you while you are packing and leaving home. He will stay in the **hotel** with you (don't worry, it does not cost more money 😜)! And he will see the sights with you until you **return home**.

A Travel Diary – The Beginning!

Going to Germany!!!

How did you get to Germany?

By plane / ship / car / other _____

We will stay in Germany for _____ days.

Is this your first visit ? yes / no

Where will you sleep? In a hotel / In a hostel / In a campsite /

In an apartment / With family / Other _____

What places are you planning to visit?

_____

_____

_____

What special activities are you planning to do?

_____

_____

_____

Are you excited about the trip?
This is an excitement indicator. Ask your family members how excited they are (from "not at all" up to "very, very much"), and mark each of their answers on the indicator. Leonardo has already marked the level of his excitement …

not at all   very,
                                          very much

                         Leonardo

Who is traveling?

Write down the names of the family members traveling with you and their answers to the questions.

Name: _____

Age: _____

Have you visited Germany before? yes / no

What is the most exciting thing about your upcoming trip?

_____
_____
_____

Paste a picture of your family.

Name: _____

Age: _____

Have you visited Germany before? yes / no

What is the most exciting thing about your upcoming trip?

_____
_____
_____

Name: _____

Age: _____

Have you visited Germany before? yes / no

What is the most exciting thing about your upcoming trip?

_____
_____
_____

Name: _____

Age: _____

Have you visited Germany before? yes / no

What is the most exciting thing about your upcoming trip?

_____
_____
_____

Name: _____

Age: _____

Have you visited Germany before? yes / no

What is the most exciting thing about your upcoming trip?

_____
_____
_____

MÜNCHEN
BAYERN
13 MAI 2011
MUNICH FRANZ JOSEF STRAUSS AIRPORT
FLUGHAFEN MÜNCHEN-FRANZ-JOSEF STRAU

FRANKFURT

Preparations at home – DO NOT FORGET ...!

Mom or Dad will take care of packing clothes (how many pairs of pants, which comb to take …). Leonardo will only tell you the stuff he thinks you might want to bring along on your trip to Germany.

Leonardo made a Packing List for you. Check off each item as you pack it!

☐ *Kids' Travel Guide — Germany* —of course 😉
☐ Comfortable walking shoes
☐ A raincoat or umbrella (Sometimes it rains without warning.)
☐ A hat (and sunglasses, if you want)
☐ Pens and pencils
☐ Crayons and markers (It is always nice to color and paint.)
☐ A notebook or writing pad (You can use it for games or writing, or to draw or doodle in when you're bored …)
☐ A book to read
☐ Your smartphone/tablet or camera

MÜNCHEN
BAYERN
13 MAI 2011
MUNICH FRANZ JOSEF STRAUSS AIRPORT
FLUGHAFEN MÜNCHEN-FRANZ JOSEF STRAUß

FRANKFURT

Pack your things in a small bag (or backpack).

You may also want to take these things:

Snacks, fruit, candy, and chewing gum.
If you are flying, it can help a lot during
takeoff and landing, when there's pressure
in your ears.

Games you can play **while sitting down:**
electronic games, booklets of crossword
puzzles, connect-the-numbers
(or connect-the-dots), etc.

Now let's see if you can find 12
items you should take on a trip in
this word search puzzle:

- ☐ Leonardo
- ☐ walking shoes
- ☐ hat
- ☐ raincoat
- ☐ crayons
- ☐ book
- ☐ pencil
- ☐ camera
- ☐ snacks
- ☐ fruit
- ☐ patience
- ☐ good mood 😉

P	A	T	I	E	N	C	E	A	W	F	G
E	L	R	T	S	G	Y	J	W	A	T	O
Q	E	Y	U	Y	K	Z	K	M	L	W	O
H	O	S	N	A	S	N	Y	S	K	G	D
A	N	R	Z	C	P	E	N	C	I	L	M
C	A	M	E	R	A	A	W	G	N	E	O
R	R	A	I	N	C	O	A	T	G	Q	O
Y	D	S	G	I	R	K	Z	K	S	H	D
S	O	A	C	O	A	E	T	K	H	A	T
F	R	U	I	T	Y	Q	O	V	O	D	A
B	O	O	K	F	O	H	Z	K	E	R	T
T	K	Z	K	A	N	S	I	E	S	Y	U
O	V	I	E	S	S	N	A	C	K	S	P

Welcome to Germany!

The name for Germany in the German language is Deutschland.
So, as they say in German, "Willkomen in Deutschland!" Welcome to Germany!

As you're about to find out, Germany is a beautiful place, whether you're in the city or the country. Over 400 million people visit Germany each year, and now you're one of them!

Germany has almost **100 nature preserves**, including the **Black Forest** where you can see mountains and woods. Some of these preserves have **beaches** or **islands**, and many of them have animals you probably won't see anywhere else—like the little owls at the Bliesgau Reserve.

Of course, Germany isn't just nature. There are lots of big, fancy cities too. In many ways, Germany's not that different from other countries. Still, there's something magical here. Maybe it's all the castles …

Now let's start our adventure! Leonardo can't wait. 😉

Who knows what continent Germany is on? (The answer is on the next page.)

Did you know?
Germany's nickname is **Land der Dichter und Denker**. That means "Land of Poets and Thinkers."

Quizzes!

How many people visit Germany each year?
A. 150 million
B. Over 400 million
C. 70 million

Answer: B. Over 400 million!

Germany on the map

Where is Germany on the map?
You can find Germany right in the center of Europe. It shares a border with *nine* other countries—can you believe that?

Germany doesn't have a **famous shape** like Italy (the boot) or Norway (the spoon). But Leonardo thinks Germany's shape looks like **a unicorn's head** (Denmark is its horn)! What do you think it looks like?

Did you know?
Germany has the second largest population in Europe. Only Russia has more people.

Can you point out Germany? Go over Germany's borders and mark them.

What is a compass rose?

A compass rose is a drawing that shows the directions: North-South-East-West. A compass rose is drawn on the face of a compass, and the needle always points North.

If you are using a map, North is always marked, so you can always figure out where the other directions are.

When you know where each direction is, it's easier to figure out where you are—and how to get to where you want to be.

Help Leonardo write down the three missing directions in the blank boxes.

North

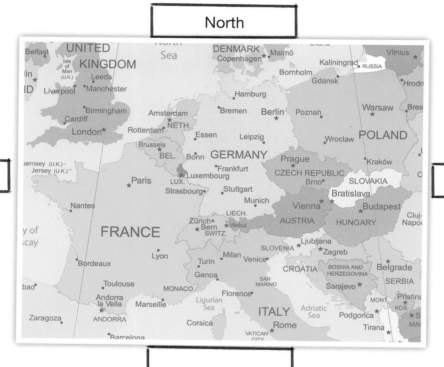

Help Leonardo read the map.

How many neighbors does Germany have to the NORTH? _____

Find the largest country that touches Germany. _____

Name a country that touches Germany's EASTERN side. _____

Answers: One—Denmark; France is the largest; on the EAST—Austria, Czech Republic, or Poland.

Germany's beautiful borders

Did you know?
Borders were invented to **separate different countries**. A border is a line that marks the end of one country's territory and the beginning of another. There are all kinds of borders. Sometimes **a river** or **a mountain** range makes **a natural border**. And sometimes **a fence** or a special **gate** marks a border. Part of Germany's eastern border is a natural border—the Oder River. The river runs 187 kilometers (116 miles) along the border between Germany and Poland.

Even though Germany is bordered by nine other countries, it's **not landlocked**. It touches two seas. Can you find them on the map? (Check page 11, Germany on the Map, for a hint!)

The sea to the northwest of Germany: _____

The sea to the northeast of Germany: _____

Answers: North Sea to the northwest; Baltic Sea to the northeast.

E	I	L	M	O	M	G	S	J	N	Z	K	N	L	M
O	N	J	R	S	Y	F	T	U	A	N	K	E	F	U
L	X	G	L	P	V	J	R	M	K	Z	K	D	X	N
Y	G	G	O	R	W	E	X	A	D	B	Y	S	C	I
S	K	S	V	L	M	F	G	X	N	I	Y	E	N	C
T	X	Z	D	B	O	T	B	A	P	K	R	R	L	H
U	K	G	E	L	U	C	J	E	Q	A	F	D	K	W
T	F	R	Z	K	K	H	B	T	R	X	O	U	E	V
T	G	Z	S	S	D	U	S	S	E	L	D	O	R	F
G	R	U	B	M	A	H	G	O	Q	L	I	A	N	T
A	C	E	T	V	W	Z	I	S	V	N	Q	N	F	K
R	V	S	Y	I	C	E	C	N	U	O	T	I	D	I
T	J	B	Q	X	L	L	E	I	P	Z	I	G	N	D
Z	U	C	U	C	N	Y	N	N	S	I	S	F	E	N
Y	J	I	N	K	R	T	O	Y	L	I	F	A	O	J

You are about to visit beautiful Germany.
Can you find 10 German cities in the word search puzzle?

- ☐ Berlin
- ☐ Frankfurt
- ☐ Hamburg
- ☐ Cologne
- ☐ Stuttgart
- ☐ Munich
- ☐ Dusseldorf
- ☐ Nuremberg
- ☐ Dresden
- ☐ Leipzig

Berlin—a capital idea!

Berlin is the **capital of Germany**! It's home to museums, universities, and many big businesses. It also hosts the largest film festival in the world! It's called the **Berlinale**.

Berlin is full of history. You'll see many historic places, such as the remains of the **Berlin Wall**. The wall used to divide the city into East and West Berlin.

Another thing you might notice in Berlin are the big **pink pipes** running above the ground. They're not enclosed water slides 😊 ... They pump water out of the ground so buildings don't sink.

Did you know that Berlin has the most famous gate in the world? It's called the **Brandenburg Gate**—but it's really just 12 big columns holding up a roof. The statue on top was once stolen by the French emperor Napoleon! (Luckily they got it back. 😊) The **Brandenburg Gate is over 200 years old.** During that time, it's been the place for many important events and speeches.

Did you know?
Berlin has the largest train station in Europe.

Did you know?
Because the German pronunciation of Berlin sounds like "**Bear-lin,**" bears are the symbol of the city. That's why you can see **bear statues everywhere,** painted in crazy colors.

Munich—the jewel of Bavaria!

Munich is the capital of Bavaria, one of Germany's states. Leonardo thinks you should know that when most people think about German traditions, they're really thinking of Bavaria.

People are familiar with things like Oktoberfest, Munich's beer-brewing festival. It started in the 1800s. And every year, millions of people come to Munich for Oktoberfest.

They wear traditional Bavarian clothing like *lederhosen* (leather shorts with suspenders) and *dirndls* (dresses with short sleeves and gathered skirts). They listen to **folk music** and eat traditional food, like lots of soft, warm **pretzels**. They also hold a parade, and there are carnival rides. It's a lot of fun! 😉

How many words can you make from "Oktoberfest"?
1. Example: "took"
2. _____
3. _____
4. _____
5. _____

Besides Oktoberfest, Munich is also known for being a home to famous artists—painters, writers, and musicians. Have you heard of **Mozart** or **Richard Wagner**? They're just two of the famous composers who came to Munich long ago to have their music performed.

Mozart

Quizzes!

How long has Munich been celebrating Oktoberfest?
- **A.** For 70 years
- **B.** For 10 years
- **C.** For 200 years

Answer: C.

Hamburg—city on the river!

Hamburg is the second biggest city in Germany. You can find it on the river Elbe.

Hamburg's port on the river is the second largest port in all of Europe. Ten million containers may be shipped through the port in a single year!

The goods in those containers used to be traded in the area of Hamburg called *Speicherstadt*, the "city of warehouses." It was built in 1883. Today many of the buildings are still used as warehouses, where they store everything from cocoa to electronics.

Quizzes!

You're a great map reader by now. Can you look on the map and find what part of Germany Hamburg is in?
A. The north
B. The east
C. The south

Have you ever seen a **model railroad**? That's Leonardo's favorite part of the Speicherstadt. The Miniatur Wunderland is a model train set, but it's probably bigger than any you've ever seen. It has 1,000 trains. They can travel over 15,000 meters (50,525 feet) of track! The tracks go through small models of German cities and even other countries. 😲

Did you know?
Some people believe hamburgers were named after the city. They think hamburgers started with Hamburg's *Frikadeller*. It was a meat patty like a hamburger—except it was served without a bun … (Americans added that!)

Frankfurt—a modern city that's very old!

Frankfurt is a very old city, and there's a lot of history to see. Even the zoo is 150 years old. (The animals are much younger, though! 😊) The city has over 100 festivals. Many have been around since the Middle Ages. That means they're at least 500 years old—a long time for a festival!

Tip! Do you want to see almost all of Frankfurt at once? If so, head to the top of the **Main Tower**.

Did you know?
An interchange is a place where several big roads meet. Frankfurt's interchange is one of the busiest in Europe. It's used by 320,000 cars every day!

Do you like to see cool dinosaur skeletons? Be sure to visit **the Senckenberg Museum**. It has loads of fossils and models of animals like dinosaurs.

Tip!
If your family just wants to see the sights, take a ride on the **Apple Wine Express**! It's a streetcar that goes around the city so you can see all the local attractions, like the zoo and the Children's Museum. And best of all, you'll get free apple juice and pretzels with your ride.

Did you know?
Hot dogs are sometimes called frankfurters! Like Leonardo, you may be wondering why ... Does it have something to do with the city? It does! You see, Frankfurt is known for a dish called *Frankfurter wuerstchen*. It's a sausage that's smaller than regular sausages— more like the size of a hot dog.

Do you like frankfurters (hot dogs)? What do you like to put on them?

Ketchup _____

Mustard _____

Other _____

17

Flag and symbols

This is Germany's flag. This style is known as a tricolor, which means three colors. I bet you can guess why! 😉 The three colors are **black**, **gold**, and **red**. The flag itself is called the *Bundesflagge und Handelsflagge*. That means "national and merchants' flag" in German.

Did you know?
No one is quite sure why these three colors were chosen, but they've been used since around 1848.

Did you know?
During World War II, Germany took a break from this flag and used **black**, white, and **red** flags instead. They went back to this flag in 1949 after the war was over.

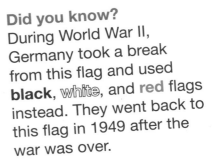

This is the symbol of Germany. It's a coat of arms that features the *Bundesadler*, which means "Federal Eagle" in German.

As you can see, the coat of arms features a gold field with a black eagle who looks as if he's showing off his muscles. He has a red beak, tongue, and feet.

Tip!

When you see the word *Bundes* in German, it means something that has to do with the government.

This eagle design has been used since 1950—but Germany has used the black eagle as a symbol for much longer than that. The modern design is not that different from some of the early ones, which are almost 1,000 years old!

If you see the tricolor German flag with the **Bundesadler seal** in the middle, that means it's a government flag. Only the government is allowed to use it.

Coins in your pocket!

Germany uses the euro for its money, just like other countries in the European Union. The euro paper money is the same in every country. It has pictures of the styles of European arches and bridges throughout history. But the coins are different in each country. That's because the countries all put their own designs on the "tails" side of euro coins.

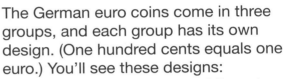

The German euro coins come in three groups, and each group has its own design. (One hundred cents equals one euro.) You'll see these designs:

- On 1-cent, 2-cent, and 5-cent coins—an oak twig;
- On 10-cent, 20-cent, and 50-cent coins—the **Brandenburg Gate in Berlin**;
- And on 1-euro and 2-euro coins—the German eagle.

Can you connect the coins in the picture to their descriptions?

And what about the "heads" side of euro coins?
All countries have the same picture on the "heads" side. It's a map of Europe with the worth of the coin printed next to it.

Quizzes!

Leonardo has a handful of the different German euro coins. He wants to buy a soft pretzel, which costs **€1.25** (1 euro and 25 cents). He wants to pay using the **fewest number** of coins, and he wants to pay the **exact amount**. What coins should he give the vendor?

Answer: Leonardo should give the vendor these coins: 1-euro, 20-cent, and 5-cent.

19

A brief history of Germany!

Early days

People started living in the area that became Germany a long time ago—during the Bronze Age. (That's when people started making tools out of bronze.) That was almost 5,000 years ago, so let's fast-forward a little. We'll start our history a bit closer to today—with **King Henry the Fowler** in 919.

He became the king of **East Francia**, a place that would become known as the **Kingdom of Germany**.

Obviously, Germany wasn't the country we know today. It was a loose assortment of different states, duchies, little kingdoms, and principalities.

Legend of the German crown offered to Henry, (painting by Hermann Vogel)

Otto von Bismarck

One country

Finally in 1871, a politician named **Otto von Bismarck** brought all those different places together. They became one country—the German Empire.

But this didn't happen by accident. Bismarck had carefully planned it. He did it by making alliances (political friendships). The leader of the new German Empire was **Kaiser Wilhelm I**. (*Kaiser* means "emperor" in German.)

Wilhelm I (painting by Emil Hunten)

Did you know?
"Duchies" are territories ruled by dukes or duchesses. "Principalities" are ruled by princes—not principals! 😊

German history ...
Modern times

The German Empire started to become a **modern country**. The nation industrialized, which means they **built factories and railroads**. Like other modern countries in Europe, Germany started **trying to get more land—and more stuff** (like diamonds!)—in places like Africa and Asia. European countries would get into **big arguments** over these faraway territories.

Berlin, 1900

So the countries started **forming alliances** with each other. When different countries make alliances, it means they agree to help each other. Sometimes it just means they will trade with each other. But it can also mean that they'll help each other fight countries that aren't in their alliance. Germany, for example, formed what they called **the Triple Alliance** with Austria and Italy. (Shhh—it was a secret ...) 😲

All these **alliances got tangled**. It didn't help when the countries started arguing over land right there in Europe. Their arguments got so big, it led to World War I in 1914.

Quizzes!

Can you guess what the members of an alliance are called? (Hint: It comes from the word "alliance.")

A. Alley cats
B. Alligators
C. Allies
D. Alibaba

Answer: C.

21

German history ... World Wars

World War I

World War I **lasted four years**, and it was huge.
It ended up pulling in countries that weren't even in Europe, like Japan and the United States. In all, **70 million people fought** all over the globe.

When the dust had settled, the Central Powers—which included Germany—had lost. They had to sign a peace treaty called the **Treaty of Versailles**.

Germany between wars

Germany's leader, Kaiser Wilhelm II, was forced to abdicate. (That means he had to quit being in charge.) The new government was called the Weimar Republic. (That's because its first meeting was held in the German city of Weimar.) A lot of people didn't like the new government, and they wanted different leaders. So they got Adolf Hitler and the Nazi (political) Party. The Nazis promised to help Germany, but they lied.

The signing of the Treaty of Versailles.

Did you know?
So many German men were killed in World War I that after the war, only one of every three German women could find a husband! 😯

You'd think grown-ups would learn their lesson, but they sometimes have to learn it again, like kids do. So a little more than 10 years after World War I, **history repeated itself**. A new worldwide war began.

As you might expect, this was called **World War II**. It started in 1939 and ended in 1945. **Germany lost again.**

German history ...
Germany gets cut in half

World War II

World War II was **even bigger** than the First World War. One hundred million people in 30 different countries fought each other. 😲 Germany was trying to get as much land as possible, and they wanted **only German people** to live there. By then, Hitler had become **a dictator**—which means he had total control and nobody could do anything unless he said so.

Hitler and the Nazi Party blamed Jewish people for all the problems Germany had after it lost World War I. So the Nazi government passed laws **punishing Jews**. The Nazis sent Jewish people to prisons called **concentration camps**. In the camps, the Jews were forced to work long hours, and many of them were killed. In fact, six million Jewish people were killed during the war. That is called the **Holocaust**.

Concentration camp Auschwitz, Poland

The Cold War

After the war, the fighting still wasn't over. The Soviet Union and the West (countries like the United States and the United Kingdom) kept arguing. In fact, they argued so much that they ended up dividing Germany right in two! The country became **East Germany** and **West Germany**, and the **Berlin Wall** separated them.

The United States and the Soviet Union would keep fighting for years. It was called the **"Cold War"** because they never fought each other in a real war with weapons. Finally in the 1980s, they started trying to be **friends again**. One part of their friendship pact? Helping Germany tear down the Berlin Wall. It fell in 1989, and the German people were so happy. Finally, they were reunited! They've been **one country** ever since. (And the Cold War ended in 1991.)

Can you put these events and people in the order they happened?

(1) Henry the Fowler

The Triple Alliance

Otto von Bismarck

The Cold War

World War II

World War I

Answers: 1-Henry the Fowler; 2-Otto von Bismarck; 3-The Triple Alliance; 4-World War I; 5-World War II; 6-The Cold War.

Culture and customs

German people are considered to be **very serious**, but really, they just like to have **everything in order**. That means they think it's very important to follow the rules—so be on your best behavior! In addition, make sure that you're on time. Germans believe it's **bad manners to be late**.

Although they're thought of as serious, Germans are **very friendly**. They like order, but they also like *gemütlichkeit*. That means a feeling of cozy friendliness, where everyone is welcome.

One way they celebrate this is with a traditional **afternoon break**—sort of like teatime in England. Between lunch and dinner, German people often gather to have a cup of coffee and a sweet, like cake. This is sometimes called *Kaffee und Kuchen* (coffee and cake) or *Kaffeetrinken* (coffee-drinking). And it's a good time to catch up with friends and family.

Of course, holidays are a good time too. The biggest holiday in Germany is Christmas. Before the holiday, many cities have **Christmas markets**. These are big street fairs where you can buy handmade presents and eat yummy treats like gingerbread and candied almonds. 😊

Traditional Christmas market in the historic center of Frankfurt, Germany.

What are three things that are special about your country's culture and holidays?

_____

_____

Fairy tale *Germany*

Have you heard of the Brothers Grimm?

You definitely know them if you know fairy tales. But if you don't, they are brothers **Jacob and Wilhelm Grimm**. They were born in Hanau, Germany, a year apart. Jacob's the oldest. He was born in 1785.

They became interested in **German folktales**. (These are old stories that people told to each other without writing them down.) The Grimm brothers started writing down the folktales. They published their first book in 1812.

It was called *Kinder- und Hausmärchen* (Children's and Household Tales). You know it better as *Grimm's Fairy Tales*. It has over 200 stories.

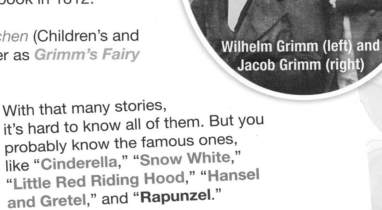

Wilhelm Grimm (left) and Jacob Grimm (right)

With that many stories, it's hard to know all of them. But you probably know the famous ones, like "**Cinderella**," "**Snow White**," "**Little Red Riding Hood**," "**Hansel and Gretel**," and "**Rapunzel**."

Today, people believe the book and its stories played an important part in building Western culture. The book also inspired writers in other countries to start collecting their own lands' fairy tales. You may have heard of some of them, like Denmark's Hans Christian Andersen.

Unscramble these fairy tales:

1. Nreladelci _____
2. Pznarlue _____
3. Wnso ewtih _____

What's your favorite fairy tale? _____

Answers: 1. Cinderella; 2. Rapunzel; 3. Snow White.

25

Famous Germans you may know

You've learned about the history of Germany and some of its famous leaders. Now it's time to meet more famous Germans …

Pleased to meet you, **Albert Einstein**

You may have heard of Einstein already, even if you're not quite sure who he is. That's because he's very famous!

Einstein was a physicist.* He's best known for developing the **theory of relativity**. Basically, he helped create the study of modern physics. He won the Nobel Prize for Physics in 1921. Einstein died in 1955. But he's considered one of the most important and **famous physicists** in the whole world!

*Physics is the science of how objects (matter) move through space and time.

What does the name "Einstein" mean to YOU? _____

Do you love classical music?
Ludwig van Beethoven

Beethoven (say "bay-toe-ven") was a famous composer. He wrote symphonies, sonatas, operas, and other classical music. He was also **a pianist**, but today we remember him more for the **music he wrote**. Beethoven began to lose his hearing in his 20s, but he continued to write music for the rest of his life.

Do you know other famous composers (maybe from other countries or even other times)?

_____
_____
_____

Did you know?
Beethoven was one of three famous composers in Germany whose names started with **B**. The others were Johann Sebastian **Bach** and Johannes **Brahms**.

Even more famous Germans ...

Have you heard about **Wernher von Braun?**

Von Braun was a **rocket scientist**. He started building rockets when he was a teenager, and he dreamed about space travel.

During World War II, the German government gave him the opportunity and supplies to build real-life rockets. When it became clear the war was ending, von Braun surrendered to American troops. They took him back to the United States, where he helped build US rockets that put men on the moon. 😮

The story of **Anne Frank**

Anne was a kid who was born in Germany. Her family was Jewish, so they left Germany for the Netherlands when Hitler took power. But when Anne was almost 11, Germany took over the Netherlands. The Franks **had to hide** so the Nazis wouldn't find them. They moved into secret rooms hidden behind a bookcase in her father's office building. Anne had started **keeping a diary** by then. After two years of hiding, the Franks **were caught** and taken to a concentration camp. There, Anne got sick and died. Her diary was saved though. It was returned to her father, who published it. *The Diary of Anne Frank* is a world-famous book. It shows what life was like for Jewish Europeans during World War II.

Here are some more famous Germans. Do you know what each of them is famous for?
Draw a line between the person's name and what they do.

Angela Merkel   Model
Boris Becker   Fashion designer
Heidi Klum   German prime minister
Michael Schumacher   Race car driver
Karl Lagerfeld   Actor
Til Schweiger   Tennis player

Answers: Angela Merkel – German prime minister; Boris Becker – tennis player; Heidi Klum – model; Michael Schumacher – race car driver; Karl Lagerfeld – fashion designer; Til Schweiger – actor.

Mahlzeit!
Enjoy German food!
Now let's learn about German meals ...

Breakfast (Frühstück)
An old-fashioned German breakfast starts with coffee or tea, although you can choose cocoa or juice (*Saft*) if you prefer. As for food, there's usually bread with spreads like honey or butter—along with sausage (*Wurst*), cheese (*Käse*), and eggs (*Eier*). However, Germans today are just as likely to reach for cereal and milk (*Milch*).

Snacks
Do you have a snack at school? So do German children! Because they usually eat lunch at home instead of at school, German children eat snacks to keep them going till lunch. Snack time is called **Grosse Pause**, **Zweites Frühstück**, or **Pausenbrot** (second breakfast). The snacks are probably a lot like yours: fruit, yogurt, and granola bars.

Of course, adults also have to keep their energy up, so they may have a snack—called **Zwischenmahlzeit**—during the day too.

Lunch (*Mittagessen*)
Lunch has traditionally been the biggest meal of the day for Germans. It is a large hot meal, usually eaten between noon and 2:00 p.m.

Evening meal (Abendbrot)
Today, some Germans eat their biggest meal at dinner. But for Germans who still have a traditional evening meal, dinner is a lot like breakfast. They eat breads, cheese, and sliced meat. You may order juice or sparkling mineral water (*Mineralwasser*) to drink with this meal.

What's your favorite meal of the day?

German cuisine (cooking)
Mahlzeit! (Bon appetit)

As in other countries, Germany's food is influenced by its neighbors. For example, in Badem-Wuerttemberg near the French border, the foods eaten are similar to traditional **French foods**. They include things like wine and snails. (Yes, snails! 😳) On the other hand, Bavaria is closer to Austria, so it comes as no surprise that Bavarian food is a lot like **Austrian food**.

German people eat many things that come from other places. Thanks to Turkish immigrants, for example, Doner Kebab is very popular in Germany. (It's basically meat on a stick!) 😋

Do you love sausages?

Well then, you've come to the right place! Germans eat a lot of sausage, mainly made of pork. Now Leonardo's going to take you on a sausage tour, so that you can pick the best ones for you (and your family).

Did you know? Germany has over 1,500 different kinds of sausage (Wurst)!

Sausage in Germany is called *Wurst*, so if you see that word in a food's name, you know you're getting sausage.

Now let's go and explore those delicious sausages!

Bratwurst: Most bratwurst are served in a roll (just like a hot dog) and topped with mustard.

Nurnberger Rostbratwurst: These sausages are only about the size of your pinkie finger!

The short, stubby *Knackwurst* is another sausage that's just your size.

Blutwurst, or blood sausage, is made of pig's or cow's blood, so it's the perfect sausage to dare your parents to eat. Be sure to take lots of funny pictures of your parents while they're eating it!

Bon appetit!
More German cuisine (cooking)

Germans don't eat just sausage, of course. They also eat a lot of vegetables.

Potatoes are very popular, especially **potato salad**, called *Kartoffelsalat* in German. Have you had German potato salad before?

Another vegetable popular in Germany is asparagus. They especially like **white asparagus**, which they call *Spargel*. They even have a special word, *Spargelzeit*. It means the time from late spring to early summer when asparagus is in season.

You've almost certainly had sauerkraut. German people eat cabbage in different ways, but **sauerkraut** (fermented cabbage) is the most well-known.

Do you like sauerkraut?

Yes _____

No way! _____

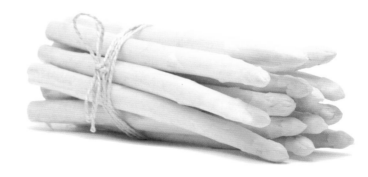

 What's your favorite German dish?

_____

Where and how to eat ...
German table manners

Here are some tips on table manners, so you'll know **how to behave**— whether you're at a restaurant or someone's home.

At the dinner table:
- Germans don't eat many foods with their hands, so **use a fork to eat your fries**.
- A sit-down meal is eaten with both a **knife and fork**, so make sure you use both if you're given a knife. Germans keep the knife in their right hand and the fork in their left hand. They use the knife to help get food onto the fork.
- It's considered bad table manners to eat with your **elbows on the table** or to put your hand in your lap.
- Make sure to compliment the home cook or chef by saying, **"Das schmeckt gut/lecker/wunderbar."** That means "It tastes good/yummy/wonderful)."

At the restaurant:
- Unless the restaurant is fancy, you can just **seat yourself**.
- At many informal restaurants, it's perfectly OK to **sit with strangers** who have open seats at their table. Just ask, "Ist hier noch frei?" ("Is this seat free?")
- If you want a cold drink, you'll have to ask for ice. There are **no free refills**—if you want another drink, you'll have to pay for it.
- If you want to take a break for a moment, **cross your knife and fork** on your plate. If you're finished eating, put them side by side. Your server will then take away your plate.

What two utensils should you use when you eat in Germany?
- **A.** Spoon and knife
- **B.** Fork and chainsaw
- **C.** Knife and fork

Which of these is consider bad manners?
- **A.** Complimenting the chef
- **B.** Putting your elbows on the table
- **C.** Eating with a knife and fork instead of your hands

Answers: C. Knife and fork; B. Elbows on the table.

And now the best part—desserts!

So now you know a little more about what Germans traditionally eat. But those aren't the only foods … We didn't get to dessert yet!

You will certainly want to eat dessert when you come to Germany. Leonardo's favorite dessert is *Lebkuchen*, which you know better as gingerbread. He also likes *Apfelkuchen* (apple cake). Are either of those your favorite—or are you more a fan of Black Forest cake (or *Schwarzwälder Kirschtorte*)?

My favorite food in Germany was _____

Where did you eat it? Who were you with? _____

Did you try something in Germany you'd never eaten before? If so, describe it. _____

Quizzes!

Food trivia!

1. What is the German word for sausage? _____
2. Germans have a special name for what vegetable's season? _____
3. What do Germans call lunch? _____
4. Name a drink that Germans traditionally have with breakfast. _____
5. What kind of sausage is made from blood? _____
6. What is traditionally the biggest meal of the day? _____

Answers: 1. Wurst; 2. White asparagus or Spargel; 3. Mittagessen; 4. Coffee, tea, cocoa, or juice; 5. Blutwurst or blood sausage; 6. Lunch or Mittagessen.

How do you say it in German ...?
A dictionary just for you!

German may seem like a hard language, but it's actually easier than you might think. Let's prove it! Many of those scary German words are just **smaller words** crammed together to make a new one. Take a German word you already know—kindergarten. It's just the word for child (kinder) and garden (garten) smushed together. Words like this are called **compound words**. And in German, they can be as long as 79 letters! Now let's learn some German!

English	German	How to say it
Hello	Hallo	how-loh
Good morning	Guten Morgen	goot-en mor-gen
Good day	Guten Tag	goot-en tahk
Good evening	Guten Abend	goot-en ah-bent
Goodbye	Auf Wiedersehen	owf vee-dair-zayn
Bye	Tschues	tchews
See you later	Bis spaeter	biss shpay-ter
How are you? (formal*)	Wie geht es Ihnen?	vee gayt es ee-nen
How are you? (informal)	Wie gehts?	Vee gayts
Good	Gut	goot
What's your name? (formal)	Wie heißen Sie?	vee hi-zun zee
What's your name? (informal)	Wie heißt du?	vee hi-zt doo
My name is …	Ich heiße …	ikh hi-zuh
Yes	Ja	yah
No	Nein	nine
Please	Bitte	bit-tuh
Thank you	Danke	dahn-kuh
You're welcome	Bitte schoen	bit-tuh shurn

Tip!

*German has formal and informal—or "everyday"—ways to speak to people. Use formal words with people older than you or people you don't know well.

33

Counting and colors
and more—in German

Colors (Die Farben)

black—schwartz (shvahrts)
white—weiß (vice)
grey—grau (grou*)
red—rot (roht)
blue—blau (blou*)
green—grün (groon)
yellow—gelb (gelp)
orange—orange (oh-RAHNGSH)
purple—lila (lee-la)
pink—rosa (roh-za)
brown—braun (brown)

Numbers (Die Nummern)

0—null (null)
1—eins (eye-ns)
2—zwei (sveye)
3—drei (dry)
4—vier (feer)
5—fünf (fuenf)
6—sechs (zeks)
7—sieben (zee-ben)
8—acht (akht)
9—neun (noin)
10—zehn (zayn)
100—hundert (hoon-dirt)
1,000—tausend (tou*-zent))

*rhymes with cow

Helpful phrases!
I have—Ich habe (ikh hah-buh)
I would like—Ich möchte (ikh mush-tuh)
I need—Ich brauche (ikh brow-kuh)

Quizzes!

How would you say "I would like seven, please"?

Answer: "Ich möchte sieben, bitte."

Same words—
different meanings?

German and English are different languages, of course, but they have a lot of **words in common**. Some of those shared words mean completely different things, though. Other words mean the same thing in German and English—or are close enough that you can figure it out.

Some German words are the same as English words, but have very different meanings in German:

- *Angel* is "fishing rod."
- *Bad* is "bathroom."
- *Bald* is "soon."
- *Boot* is "boat."
- *Gift* is "poison."

Here are some words that are the same—and mean the same thing—in German and English:

Alligator
Alphabet
Dessert
Name
Tiger
Finger
Butter

Same meanings—almost the same words. These German words are very close to English. Can you figure out what they mean?

1. Fisch _____
2. Bett _____
3. Sohn _____
4. Leicht _____
5. Schulter _____

Did you know?
In German, "thanks" can mean "no." So if someone asks you, "Would you like a drink?" you can say, "Danke," to mean "No, thank you."

Unscramble these words that both languages share.

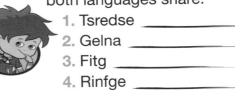

1. Tsredse _____
2. Gelna _____
3. Fitg _____
4. Rinfge _____
5. Trubet _____
6. Blpaehta _____

Answers: 1. Dessert; 2. Angel; 3. Gift; 4. Finger; 5. Butter; 6. Alphabet.

Did you know?
You may notice German words with the letter ß. It's called **an Eszett**. It's usually pronounced like the "Z" in "gaze."

Germany is famous for ...

You've learned about some famous German people and Germany's famous history. **Now it's time for famous fun facts!**

The **Autobahn** is Germany's national highway system. It was the **first high-speed freeway** in the world.

Most people know the Autobahn, though, because it has **no blanket speed limit**. That doesn't mean your bedspread can go as fast as it wants! It means there's no speed limit that everyone has to follow. Some kinds of vehicles, like buses, have to obey speed limits, but regular cars don't.

Speaking of driving, Germany is home to **some of the most famous car companies in the world**. I'm sure you've heard of at least one of them. Does **Volkswagen** or **Mercedes-Benz** or **BMW** sound familiar? How about **Porsche** or **Audi**? 😜

Germany has the second longest river in Europe, and the longest river in the European Union. It's the **Danube River**, and it starts in Germany's **Black Forest** (*Schwarzwald*). 😯

Germans love football. (If you're from North America, you call it soccer.) Germany's national team—**Die Mannschaft**—has won the World Cup four times. 😯

Do you play football (soccer)?

Over 100 Germans have won Nobel Prizes, including Albert Einstein, whom you've already "met." 😯

Did you know?
Germany's national football team is nicknamed *Nationalelf*. It means "national 11."

More fun facts about Germany ...

- Germany has **over 400 zoos**—more than any other country in the world!

- At the beginning of the 19th century (the 1800s), **fighting with swords** (**dueling**) was a popular hobby. It was considered cool to have scars from the fights. In fact, people who didn't actually fight would sometimes give themselves scars to fit in!

- The German government has strict rules about what you can **name your baby**. You can't give your child the same name as a product or use a last name as a first name. And you can't use a boy's name for a girl, or a girl's name for a boy. The civil registration office, or Standesamt, will say no to names that don't follow the rules.

- East and West Germany used different kinds of **streetlights**. That was so you could tell the difference between the countries from space! Even though Germany is now one country, the streetlights are still different in the former East and West sides.

- Germans have always been at the head of the class when it comes **to books**. They printed the first book ever around 1455. They also printed the world's first magazine in 1663. Even today, they publish around 94,000 different book titles every year!

- There are more than **150 castles** in Germany.

- **And when you have a birthday ...** Germans won't wish you a happy birthday before the actual day. They have a saying *"Du sollst den Tag nicht vor dem Abend loben,"* or "You shouldn't praise the day before the night." It means that you shouldn't celebrate something before it has actually happened, because it's bad luck.

What do you know about Germany?

By now you're an expert on Germany. Want to prove it? Try your hand at these quick questions. (Hint: All the answers can be found in this book.)

Quizzes!

1. What is Germany's money called? _____

2. What popular German food came from Turkey? _____

3. During what "Age" did people start living in the area that's now Germany? _____

4. What's the name of the politician who unified Germany into one country in 1871? _____

5. What city hosts Oktoberfest? _____

6. What German composer continued writing music even after losing his hearing? _____

7. What kind of sausage is just the size of your little finger? _____

8. What is Germany's national highway system called? _____

Answers:
1. Euros; 2. Doner kebab; 3. Bronze; 4. Otto von Bismarck; 5. Munich; 6. Beethoven; 7. Nürnberger Rostbratwurst; 8. The Autobahn

Write your own fairy tale!

Instead of collecting stories like the Grimm Brothers, why not try making up your own? Leonardo believes you can! (Hint: If you're stumped, try putting animals in it or adding some magic things.)

Name of the story: _____
Writer: _____

Put your own words in the blanks, and a great story will come out.

Yesterday morning we drove to _____ Castle. We met a talking

_____ and a dancing _____. We suggested they join us.

They said _____ and went to _____.

After we left the castle, we went to the _____. When we got

there, we saw a _____. We were pretty surprised!

At first, we thought it was _____, but pretty soon we realized

that it was _____. _____ said that the best thing would

be to _____ and we all agreed.

When we returned to the hotel, it wasn't the hotel anymore—it was

a giant _____. We were really surprised

then! We didn't know what to do. Where

were our beds? When we started walking

toward the _____, we found out

_____.

That's when I woke up in a _____, and

realized it was all a dream!

And to sum it all up ...

SUMMARY OF THE TRIP

We had great fun! What a pity it is over ...

Which places did we visit?

_____

_____

Whom did we meet ...
- Did you meet tourists from other countries? yes / no
  If you did meet tourists, where did they come from?
  (Name their nationalities):

_____

Shopping and souvenirs ...
- What did you buy on the trip?

_____

_____

- What did you want to buy, but ended up not buying?

_____

Experiences ...
- What were the most memorable experiences of the trip?

_____

_____

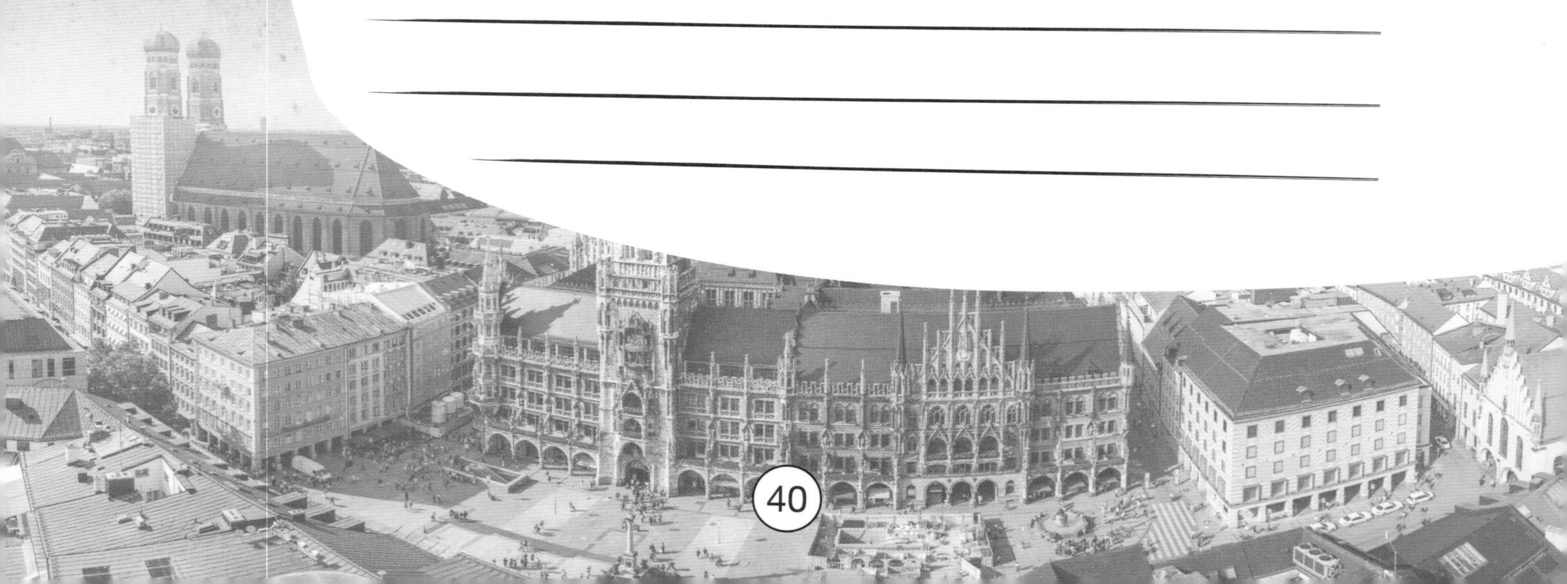

What was each family member's favorite place?

_____ : _____
_____ : _____
_____ : _____
_____ : _____

Grade the most beautiful places and the best experiences of your journey:

First place

Second place		Third place

And now, a difficult task—talk with your family and decide:

What did everyone enjoy most on the trip?

Date

What did we do?